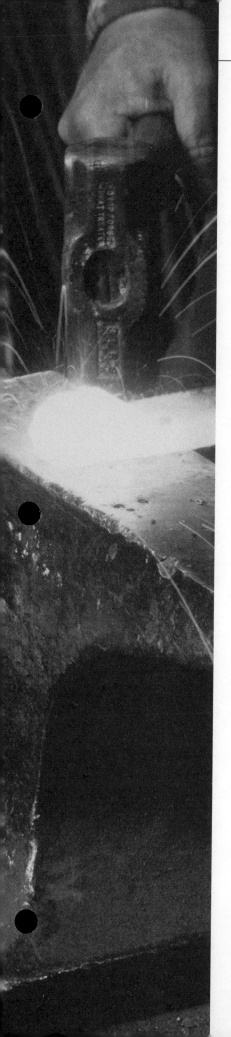

SO-AAN-327

History Alive!®
The United States
Through Industrialism

TCi™

Chief Executive Officer: Bert Bower

Chief Operating Officer: Amy Larson

Director of Curriculum: Liz Russell

Managing Editor: Laura Alavosus

Editorial Project Manager: Nancy Rogier

Project Editor: Mali Apple

Copyeditor: Jennifer Seidel

Editorial Associates: Anna Embree, Sarah Sudano

Production Manager: Lynn Sanchez

Art Director: John F. Kelly

Senior Graphic Designers: Paul Rebello, Christy Uyeno

Graphic Designers: Don Taka, Victoria Philp

Photo Edit Manager: Margee Robinson

Photo Editor: Picture Research Consultants, Inc.

Production Project Manager: Eric Houts

Art Editor: Mary Swab

TCi™

Teachers' Curriculum Institute

PO Box 1327

Rancho Cordova, CA 95741

Customer Service: 800-497-6138

www.teachtci.com

ISBN 978-1-58371-932-9

11 12 13 14 -DH- 21 20 19 18

Manufactured by Hess Print Solutions, Brimfield, OH
United States of America, April, 2018, Job #271876

Program Director
Bert Bower

Program Author
Diane Hart

Creative Development Manager
Kelly Shafsky

Contributing Writers
Laura Alavosus
John Bergez
Susan Buckley
Jill Fox
Christine Freeman
Amy George
Brent Goff
Andrew Goldblatt
David M. Holford
Elspeth Leacock
Tedd Levy
Julie Weiss

Curriculum Developers
Joyce Bartky
April Bennett
Nicole Boylan
Vern Cleary
Terry Coburn
Julie Cremin
Erin Fry
Amy George
Steve Seely
Nathan Wellborne

Reading Specialist
Kate Kinsella, Ed.D.
Reading and TESOL Specialist
San Francisco State University

Teacher Consultants
Melissa Aubuchon
City of Ladue School District
St. Louis, Missouri

Terry Coburn
Brookside School
Stockton, California

Connie Davidson
San Leandro Unified School District
San Leandro, California

Amy George
Weston Middle School
Weston, Massachusetts

Nicolle Hutchinson
Broward County Public Schools
Miramar, Florida

Dawn Lavond
Moreland Middle School
San Jose, California

Julie Peters
Woodstock Community Union School District #200
Woodstock, Illinois

Debra Schneider
Tracy Unified School District
Tracy, California

Acknowledgments

Scholars

Dr. Eric Avila
*University of California,
Los Angeles*

Maureen Booth
Maynard, Massachusetts

Dr. Eun Mi Cho
*California State University
Sacramento*

Dr. William Deverell
University of Southern California

Dr. Dan Dupre
*University of North Carolina,
Charlotte*

Dr. Ben Keppel
University of Oklahoma

Dr. Stanley J. Underdal
San Jose State University

Dr. Dan Wickburg
University of Texas, Dallas

Readability Consultant

Jeanne Barry
*Jeanne Barry and Associates, Inc.
Incline Village, Nevada*

Cartographer

Mapping Specialists
Madison, Wisconsin

Internet Consultant

Chuck Taft
*University School of Milwaukee
Milwaukee, Wisconsin*

Diverse Needs Consultants

Erin Fry
Glendora, California

Colleen Guccione
Naperville, Illinois

Cathy Hix
*Swanson Middle School
Arlington, Virginia*

UNIT **1**

Our Colonial Heritage

Geography Challenge

Chapter 1: The First Americans

How did the first Americans adapt to their environments?

Chapter 2: European Exploration and Settlement

*How did Europeans explore and establish settlements
in the Americas?*

Chapter 3: The English Colonies in North America

*What were the similarities and differences among the
colonies in North America?*

Chapter 4: Life in the Colonies

What was life really like in the colonies?

Timeline Challenge

North America

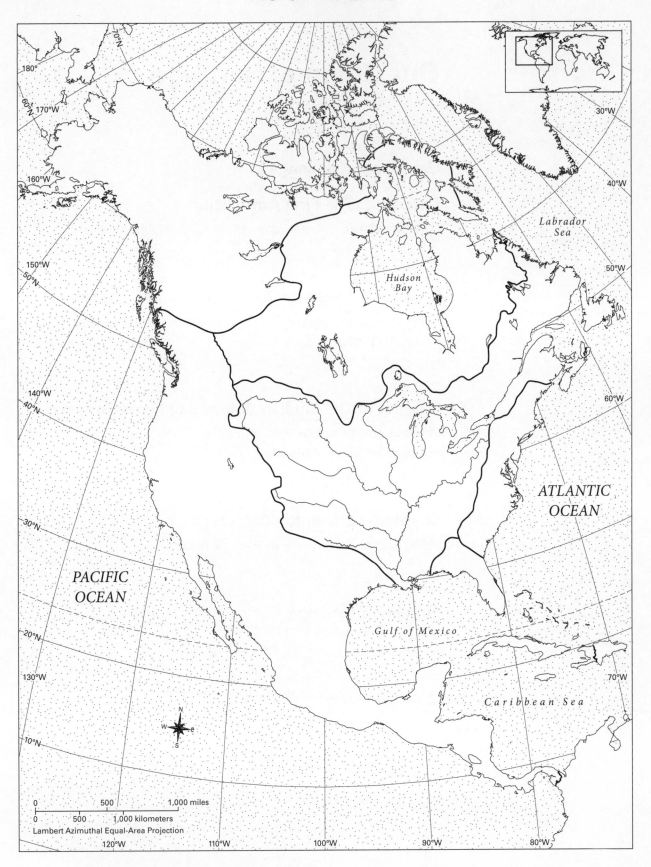

Geography Skills

Analyze the maps in "Setting the Stage" for Unit 1 in your book. Then answer the following questions and fill out the map as directed.

1. Locate the region of North America that was claimed by Spain. Shade and label it on your map.

2. Locate the area in North America that was claimed by France. Shade and label it.

3. Locate the British land claims in North America. Shade and label them.

4. Draw and label the Appalachian Mountains on your map. These mountains were mainly part of which nation's land claims?

5. Draw and label the Rocky Mountains on your map. In which nation's land claims did these mountains mainly fall?

6. Which three major rivers flow through the land claimed by France? Label them.

7. The colonies that became the original United States were part of which European nation's land claims?

   What demands did colonists in this region place on the American Indians who lived there?

8. Locate and label the other Great Lakes: Superior, Michigan, Huron, Erie, and Ontario. How did involvement with Europeans in this region change how American Indians there lived?

Critical Thinking

Answer the following questions in complete sentences.

9. In areas where physical geography made farming more difficult for British colonists, what else do you think they might have done for a living?

10. Suppose you are a settler in the British colonies. You want to settle on land where the Ohio River meets the Mississippi River. What physical feature do you have to cross to reach that area?

   Traveling over land, what might be a good route?

11. Look at the map of physical features of North America in your book. Suppose you were traveling west from the Mississippi River to the Pacific Coast. In terms of elevation, describe the land on your route westward.

   Where might farming be easiest in this western region? Why?

The First Americans

How did the first Americans adapt to their environments?

PREVIEW

Carefully examine the photograph of a Canadian forest. Imagine that you suddenly find yourself in this environment. Brush and a thick forest of fir and pine trees surround the mountain valley. It is late fall and getting cold. The pond has not yet frozen. You must survive here for a year.

On a separate sheet of paper, describe the shelter you would build, the clothing you would make to protect yourself from the elements, and the tools you would create to acquire food.

READING NOTES

Key Content Terms

As you complete the Reading Notes, use these terms in your answers.

migrate   culture

environment   cultural region

natural resource

Section 1.2

1. Define the term *Beringia* in your own words. Then draw a simple illustration to represent the term.

2. Using the map in Section 1.2, answer these questions:

   • Where did the first Americans come from?

   • Where did they migrate?

Section 1.3

1. Give two examples of how American Indians used natural resources to adapt to their environments.

2. In your own words, describe what the term *culture* means.

3. Use the maps in Section 1.3 to answer these questions:

- Which American Indian cultural region do you live in?

- What type of clothing would most American Indians living on the Plains wear?

- What type of housing would most American Indians living in the Southeast build?

- What type of food would most American Indians living in the Great Basin eat?

Section 1.4

Read this Sioux quotation.

> *From Wakan Tanka, the Great Spirit, there came a great unifying life force that flowed in and through all things—the flowers of the plains, blowing winds, rocks, trees, birds, animals.*

What does the quotation reveal about how American Indians viewed the environment?

If your class is doing the activity for this chapter, fill in the entire matrix. Use information from the corresponding placard and reading section to complete the column for each cultural region. Give at least one example of each characteristic listed. In the last row, draw a symbol to represent the cultural region. Some answers are given for you.

(Note: If your class is not doing the activity, leave the "Placard" row blank.)

	Section 1.5: Northwest Coast	Section 1.6: California	Section 1.7: Great Basin
Placard			
Main geographic features	thick forests of fir, spruce, and cedar; rugged mountains		
Main food sources		salmon, shellfish, deer, roots, berries, pine nuts, acorns	
Types of homes			temporary shelters of willow poles shaped into a cone and covered with brush or reeds
Types of, and materials for, crafts and clothing			
Tools			
Symbol			

Section 1.8: Plateau	Section 1.9: Southwest	Section 1.10: Great Plains	Section 1.11: Eastern Woodlands	Section 1.12: Southeast
clothing from animal hides and decorated with seeds and shells; woven baskets and hats				
	corn grinders			

PROCESSING

On another sheet of paper, create an annotated diagram showing how the American Indians in one cultural region adapted to their environment. Your diagram should include

- at least two examples of the land and climate.
- at least three adaptations made by American Indians to their environment.
- at least five labels describing the land, climate, and adaptations.

An example is given for you of the Northwest Coast region.

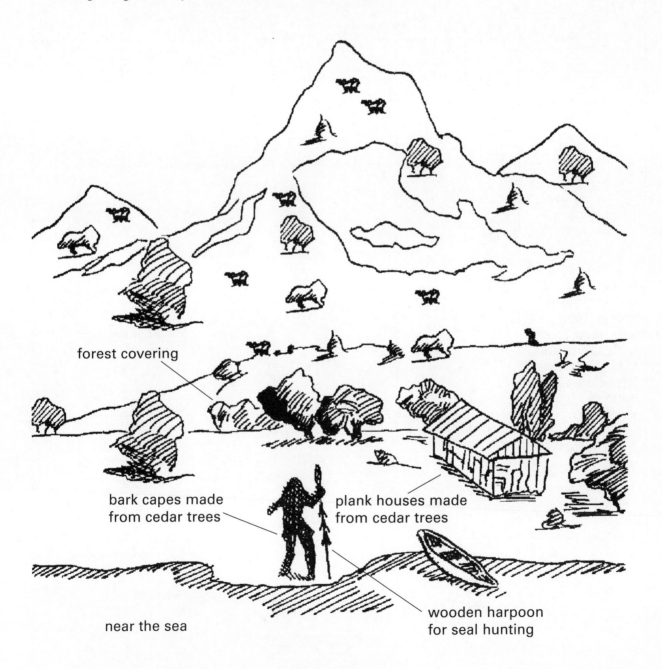

forest covering

bark capes made
from cedar trees

plank houses made
from cedar trees

wooden harpoon
for seal hunting

near the sea

© Teachers' Curriculum Institute

Preparing to Write: Asking Good Questions

The location of Cahokia is shown on the map below. List five questions people have asked about Cahokia. Also tell what tools or techniques they have used to try to answer each of those questions. An example is given for you.

Example: Thomas Jefferson asked, *Who built the mounds?* He dug up skeletons and artifacts to find an answer to his question.

1.

2.

3.

4.

5.

American Indian Cultural Regions

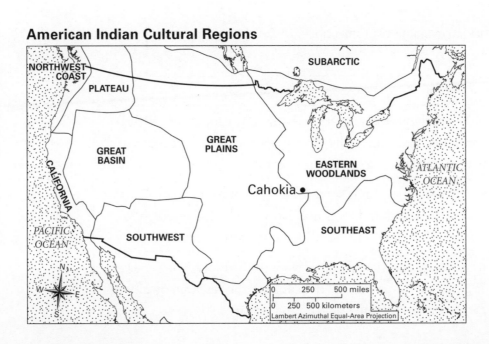

Writing Research Questions

Suppose you are an archaeologist like Tim Pauketat. Choose one of the eight geographical regions labeled on the map on the previous page. What else would you like to know about life in that region before Europeans arrived? Think of a question you would like to research.

My research question:

Write a series of questions that will help you answer your research question. Tell what tool or tools from the archaeologist's toolkit could help you answer each of those questions. An example is given for you.

Example: Did men or women build the houses?

       Tools: oral histories, witnesses

Archaeologists' Tools
oral histories
radiocarbon dating
artifacts
witnesses

Use this rubric to evaluate your questions. Make changes to your questions if you need to.

Score	Description
3	The research question is very relevant to the topic. The series of questions and tools will help answer the research question. There are no spelling or grammar errors.
2	The research question is somewhat relevant to the topic. The series of questions and tools may help answer the research question. There are some spelling or grammar errors.
1	The research question is not relevant to the topic. The series of questions and tools will not help answer the research question. There are many spelling or grammar errors.

European Exploration and Settlement

How did Europeans explore and establish settlements in the Americas?

If you were looking for a place to establish a new community, what factors would you consider? Using the list below and any other ideas you have, rank the factors from most important to least important. Then, *on another sheet of paper,* write a paragraph explaining your choice for the most and least important factors.

- fresh water source
- fertile land
- friendly neighbors
- mild climate
- near a river or ocean
- near a forest
- an area suitable for defense or spotting enemies
- other: _____

READING NOTES

Key Content Terms

As you complete the Reading Notes, use these terms in your answers.

Columbian Exchange	colony
slavery	missionaries
conquistadors	coureurs de bois

Section 2.2

1. In complete sentences, describe how Spain established territorial claims in the Caribbean and South America. Include these terms in your answer: *Christopher Columbus, conquistadors, Hernán Cortés, Francisco Pizarro.*

2. Create a simple illustration or diagram of the Columbian Exchange. Label the following items in your illustration: *people, foods, domesticated animals, diseases.*

1. Describe how Spain established territorial claims in North America. Include
    these terms in your answer: *Ponce de León, Francisco Coronado, pueblos.*

2. Create a simple illustration showing what life was like in a typical Spanish
    settlement in North America. Label the following items in your illustration:
    presidio, mission. Then describe your illustration in at least two sentences.

3. Describe the relationship that existed between the Spanish and the American
    Indians living in North America.

4. Color in and label the area of New Spain on the map on the facing page.
    Then color in the corresponding part of the key.

Follow the directions in the Reading Notes for Sections 2.3 to 2.6 to label and color code this map.

European Settlements in North and South America, 1682

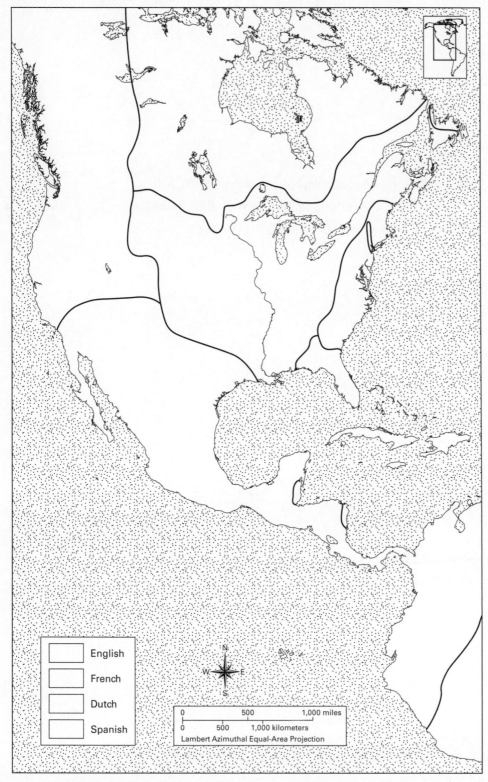

English

French

Dutch

Spanish

0   500   1,000 miles
0   500   1,000 kilometers
Lambert Azimuthal Equal-Area Projection

1. Describe how France established territorial claims in North America.
    Include these terms in your answer: *Jacques Cartier, Samuel de Champlain,
    Robert de La Salle.*

2. Create a simple illustration showing what life was like in a typical French
    settlement in North America. Label the following item in your illustration:
    coureurs de bois. Then describe your illustration in at least two sentences.

3. Describe the relationship that existed between the French and the American
    Indians living in North America.

4. Color in and label the area of New France on the map. Then color in the
    corresponding part of the key.

Section 2.5

1. Describe how England established territorial claims in North America.
   Include these terms in your answer: *John Cabot, London Company, Jamestown.*

2. Create a simple illustration showing what life was like in Jamestown.
   Then describe your illustration in at least two sentences.

3. Describe the relationship that existed between the British and the American
   Indians living in North America.

4. Color in and label the area of New England on the map. Then color in the
   corresponding part of the key.

1. Describe how the Netherlands established territorial claims in North America. Include these terms in your answer: *Henry Hudson, Peter Stuyvesant.*

2. Create a simple illustration showing what life was like in a trading post in New Netherland. Label the following items in your illustration: *fur, Iroquois, weapons.* Then describe your illustration in at least two sentences.

3. Describe the relationship that existed between the Dutch and the American Indians living in North America.

4. Color in and label the area of New Netherland on the map. Then color in the corresponding part of the key.

PROCESSING

On a separate sheet of paper, create a historical marker commemorating an early European settlement. Your marker should have

- an appropriate title.
- a brief summary that clearly explains
  (1) how the settlement was established,
  (2) how American Indians living near the

settlement were treated, and (3) how the settlement flourished or failed.

- visuals that illustrate the three main ideas of the summary.
- writing free of spelling and grammatical errors.

Preparing to Write: Analyzing Points of View

You have just read about individuals and groups who saw the same thing from different viewpoints. Summarize each of the following points of view in a few sentences.

The Encounter Between Spanish and Indians

Taino point of view:

Columbus's point of view:

Las Casas's point of view:

The Actions of Christopher Columbus

Washington Irving's point of view:

Samuel Eliot Morison's point of view:

Howard Zinn's point of view:

Writing Point-of-View Paragraphs

Choose a recent event, such as something that happened at school, an argument you had with a friend, or a news event. Write a paragraph relating your version of that event. Then imagine how someone else would see the same event. Write a second paragraph from that person's point of view.

From my point of view:

From _____'s point of view:

Use this rubric to evaluate your paragraphs. Make changes in your paragraphs if you need to.

Score	Description
3	Each paragraph presents a clear point of view and has a variety of convincing details. Each is well constructed with a topic sentence, supporting details, and a conclusion. There are no spelling or grammar errors.
2	Each paragraph presents a clear point of view and has some convincing details. Each has a topic sentence, supporting details, and a conclusion. There are some spelling or grammar errors.
1	The paragraphs do not present a clear point of view and have few convincing details. They lack topic sentences, supporting details, and conclusions. There are many spelling or grammar errors.

The English Colonies in North America

What were the similarities and differences among the colonies in North America?

PREVIEW

Examine the map of colonial America in Section 3.2 of your book. Then answer these questions *on a separate sheet of paper:*

1. What are some interesting details you notice in the map?

2. What similarities and differences existed among the colonial regions?

READING NOTES

Key Content Terms

As you complete the Reading Notes, use these terms in your answers.

mercantilism	democratic
cash crops	Mayflower Compact
charter	slave trade

Section 3.2

1. On the map, outline the New England, Middle and Southern regions in three different colors. Add your colors to the map key.

2. Underline the name of each colony that was settled in the New England, Middle, and Southern regions.

Colonial America, 1770

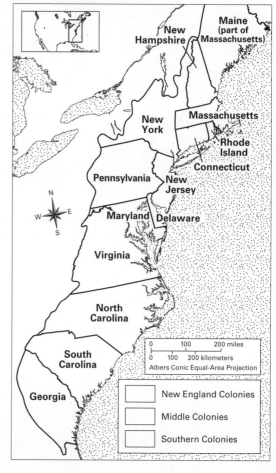

© Teachers' Curriculum Institute

3. Give at least two details about the geography, climate, or economic activities
    in each region.

    New England Colonies:

    Middle Colonies:

    Southern Colonies:

Sections 3.3 to 3.10

In each of these sections, complete the spoke diagram by describing the key features of the colony. Draw a simple symbol to represent each feature. A sample is shown here.

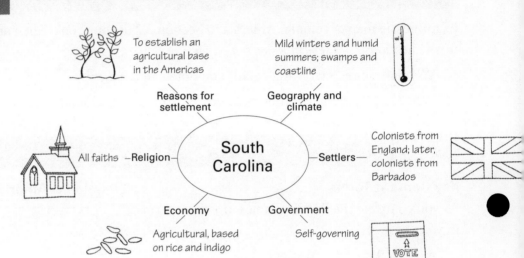

Section 3.3

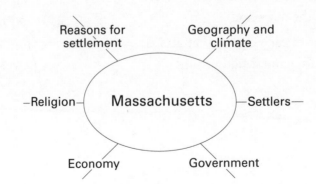

© Teachers' Curriculum Institute

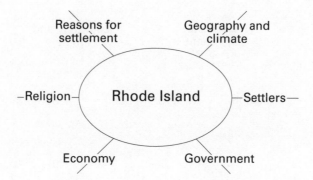

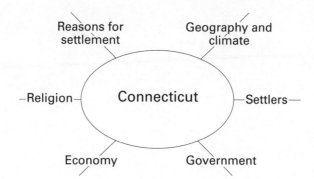

Section 3.6

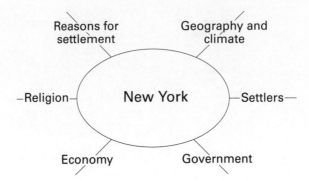

Section 3.7

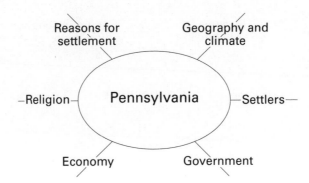

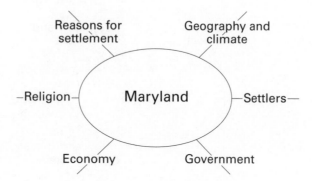

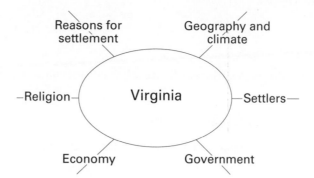

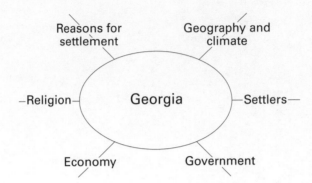

PROCESSING

Suppose you are an English colonist in the early 1700s. *On a separate sheet of paper,* write a postcard to a friend in Europe encouraging him or her to settle in your colony. Write your message on one side of the postcard, and draw a picture of your colony on the other side.

Your postcard must have

- a greeting and a closing.
- three reasons why your colony is different from other colonies and is the best place to settle.
- writing free of spelling and grammatical errors.
- a colorful illustration showing some of the colony's best features.

Preparing to Write: Analyzing Primary Source Documents

Much of what we know about the Pilgrims and Plymouth comes from the writings of William Bradford. In 1630, Bradford began writing a history called *Of Plymouth Plantation*. (Plantation was another word for colony.) The other important history of the time was *Mourt's Relation*. Written by Bradford and others in 1622, it describes the reasons for writing and signing the Mayflower Compact:

This day, before we came to harbour, observing some not well affected to unity and concord, . . . it was thought good there should be an association and agreement, that we should combine together in one body, and to submit to such government and governors as we should by common consent agree to make and choose, and set our hands to this that follows, word for word.

What problem did the Separatists see? How did they propose to solve it?

Who would choose the "government and governors"?

Bradford carefully recorded the exact words of the Mayflower Compact:

In the name of God, Amen. We, whose names are underwritten, the loyal subjects of our dread sovereigne Lord, King James, by the grace of God, of Great Britaine, France, and Ireland king, defender of the faith, etc., having undertaken, for the glory of God, and advancement of the Christian faith, and honour of our king and country, a voyage to plant the first colony in the Northerne parts of Virginia, doe by these presents, solemnly and mutually in the presence of God and one another, covenant and combine ourselves together into a civil body politick, for our better ordering and preservation and furtherance of the ends aforesaid; and by virtue hereof to enacte, constitute, and frame such just and equall laws, ordinances, acts, constitutions, and offices, from time to time, as shall be thought most meete and convenient for the generall good of the Colonie unto which we promise all due submission and obedience. In witness whereof we have hereunder subscribed our names at Cap-Codd the 11 of November, in the year of the raigne of our sovereigne lord, King James of England, France and Ireland, the eighteenth, and of Scotland the fiftie-fourth. Anno Domini, 1620.

According to the Mayflower Compact, what were the reasons for forming a government ("a civil body politick")?

What did the signers expect the government to do?

To whom did the signers promise "submission and obedience"?

Writing a Letter

Suppose you were a Separatist on the Mayflower. Write a short letter to someone still in England, describing your feelings about the Mayflower Compact.

Use this rubric to evaluate your letter. Make changes in your letter if you need to.

Score	Description
3	The letter has a clear point of view and many details. It is well constructed with correct letter format. There are no spelling or grammar errors.
2	The letter has a clear point of view and some details. It is constructed with correct letter format. There are some spelling or grammar errors.
1	The letter does not have a clear point of view or many details. It is not constructed with correct letter format. There are many spelling or grammar errors.

Life in the Colonies

What was life really like in the colonies?

PREVIEW

Suppose you are living in England in the 1700s. You have just finished reading "The Untold Story of Life in the American Colonies," a special edition of the *London Chronicle*. Below are eight headlines from this edition of the newspaper. Using a scale from 1 to 3, rate how accurate you think each headline is.

> **1:** mostly accurate   **2:** partly accurate   **3:** mostly inaccurate

_____ Study Shows Farmers Spend Several Hours Playing Cards Each Day

_____ Unemployment Rises in Cities— Colonists Return to Mother Country

_____ Colonists Ignore Principles of Self-Government

_____ African Merchants Make Fortunes Trading Cloth for Rum

_____ Preachers Stir Colonists into a Frenzy

_____ Shocking Investigation: New England Schools Lack Spelling, Reading, and Arithmetic

_____ New Survey: American Wives Say They Work Harder Than Servants

_____ Colonists Use Honeybees to Get Work Done

READING NOTES

Key Content Terms

As you complete the Reading Notes, use these terms in your answers.

rights	Parliament	Great Awakening
Magna Carta	English Bill of Rights	

Sections 4.2 to 4.9

If your class is doing the activity for this chapter, complete all the questions for these sections. *(Note: If your class is not doing the activity, skip Questions 1 and 4 in each of these sections.)*

Section 4.2

1. *Key Question:* How accurate is the headline "Study Shows Farmers Spend Several Hours Playing Cards Each Day": mostly accurate, partly accurate, or mostly inaccurate? Use evidence from Placard 4A to explain your answer.

2. What proportion of the colonial population lived on small family farms?

3. List two ways life on a farm in the 1700s was different from your life today.

4. If the headline about farm life is inaccurate, write a new, more accurate headline about this topic.

Section 4.3

1. *Key Question:* How accurate is the headline "Unemployment Rises in Cities— Colonists Return to Mother Country": mostly accurate, partly accurate, or mostly inaccurate? Use evidence from Placard 4B to explain your answer.

2. What proportion of the colonial population lived in cities?

3. Use your senses to describe life in a colonial city. Tell what you might see, hear, smell, taste, and touch there.

4. If the headline about city life is inaccurate, write a new, more accurate headline about this topic.

Section 4.4

1. *Key Question:* How accurate is the headline "Colonists Ignore Principles of Self-Government": mostly accurate, partly accurate, or mostly inaccurate? Use evidence from Placard 4C to explain your answer.

2. How did colonists see themselves? Why was this important for their rights?

3. How were the rights of English citizens strengthened during each of these years? Include the words in parentheses in your answers.

   1215 (Magna Carta, king):

   1265 (Parliament, laws):

   1689 (English Bill of Rights, taxes):

4. If the headline about colonists' rights is inaccurate, write a new, more accurate headline about this topic.

Section 4.5

1. *Key Question:* How accurate is the headline "African Merchants Make Fortunes Trading Cloth for Rum": mostly accurate, partly accurate, or mostly inaccurate? Use evidence from Placard 4D to explain your answer.

2. In which colonial regions was slavery found? In which region did it expand most rapidly, and why?

3. Why did slaves have little hope of making a better life for themselves?

4. If the headline about life for African Americans is inaccurate, write a new, more accurate headline about this topic.

1. *Key Question:* How accurate is the headline "Preachers Stir Colonists into a Frenzy": mostly accurate, partly accurate, or mostly inaccurate? Use evidence from Placard 4E to explain your answer.

2. What two adjectives best describe Puritan church services? Explain.

3. How did the Great Awakening help pave the way for the American Revolution? Follow these two steps to reveal the answer.
   - Number the sentences below from 1 to 5 to show the order in which they occurred. One of them is numbered for you.
   - Paraphrase the sentences (reword them) and write each in the correct space in the flowchart.

   Causes and Effects of the Great Awakening

   _____ These new ideas strengthened the principles of liberty, equality, and self-reliance.

   _____ There was a feeling that people had lost their religious faith.

   _____ New ideas, such as "all people are equal in the eyes of God," spread through the colonies.

   __5__ By the 1770s, colonists valued the ideals of the Great Awakening, helping pave the way for the American Revolution.

   _____ The Great Awakening began in the colonies in the 1730s.

   | 1 |
   | 2 |
   | 3 |
   | 4 |
   | 5 These ideals helped set off the American Revolution. |

4. If the headline about religion is inaccurate, write a new, more accurate headline about this topic.

Section 4.7

1. *Key Question:* How accurate is the headline "Shocking Investigation: New England Schools Lack Spelling, Reading, and Arithmetic": mostly accurate, partly accurate, or mostly inaccurate? Use evidence from Placard 4F to explain your answer.

2. Explain how education was provided in each region. Put a ★ next to the region in which people supported public education because of their religious faith.

   New England Colonies:

   Middle Colonies:

   Southern Colonies:

3. Name two ways in which a colonial school in New England was different from your school.

4. If the headline about education is inaccurate, write a new, more accurate headline about this topic.

Section 4.8

1. *Key Question:* How accurate is the headline "New Survey: American Wives Say They Work Harder Than Servants": mostly accurate, partly accurate, or mostly inaccurate? Use evidence from Placard 4G to explain your answer.

2. Give one interesting fact about colonial marriage, and tell how marriage in the United States today is different.

3. What is one reason why colonial families were so large?

4. If the headline about colonial families is inaccurate, write a new, more accurate headline about this topic.

1. *Key Question:* How accurate is the headline "Colonists Use Honeybees to Get Work Done": mostly accurate, partly accurate, or mostly inaccurate? Use evidence from Placard 4H to explain your answer.

2. Write a definition for the "bee" described in this section.

3. Draw and label two leisure activities you would have enjoyed as an American colonist.

4. If the headline about leisure is inaccurate, write a new, more accurate headline about this topic.

PROCESSING

You will now write your conclusions about the American colonies in a newspaper article entitled "What Life Is *Really* Like in the Colonies." In this article, you will correct some of the inaccurate statements that were printed in the *London Chronicle*. Write your article *on a separate piece of paper* and include

- an introductory paragraph.

- an accurate description of two or three aspects of life in the colonies. Write one paragraph for each aspect. In your descriptions, include your own conclusions. Support them with information from the primary and secondary sources and your Reading Notes.

- a short concluding paragraph about your overall understanding of life in the colonies.

- at least one image that supports your conclusions. This image can be a sketch, a tracing, or a copy of an appropriate illustration or photograph that you find.

Preparing to Write: Analyzing Speeches

In the 1730s, George II was the King of England. Few, if any, colonists questioned their loyalty to the king—even though he was more than 3,000 miles away. However, colonists soon began to think differently about the king. In less than 50 years, they would declare independence from English rule altogether.

Historians believe that some of the seeds of that new way of thinking were planted during the Great Awakening. Read these two excerpts from sermons at the time.

The wrath of kings is very much dreaded, especially of absolute monarchs, who have the possessions and lives of their subjects wholly in their power . . . But the greatest earthly potentates [rulers] in their greatest majesty and strength . . . are but feeble, despicable worms of the dust, in comparison of the great and almightly Creator and King of heaven and earth.

—Jonathan Edwards, "Sinners in the Hands of an Angry God," 1741

The essence of government (I mean good government . . .) consists in the making and executing of good laws [that provide for the common welfare] of the governed . . . We may very safely assert . . . that no civil rulers are to be obeyed when they [make laws] inconsistent with the commands of God . . . All commands running counter to the declared will of the Supreme Legislator of heaven and earth are null and void, and therefore disobedience to them is a duty, not a crime. Another thing may be [argued] with equal truth and safety, is, that no government is to be submitted to at the expense of that which is the sole end of all government—the common good and safety of society.

—Jonathan Mayhew, "A Discourse Concerning Unlimited Submission and Non-Resistance to the Higher Powers," 1750

What does Jonathan Edwards say about the power of kings?

According to Edwards, which is greater: the power of God or the power of kings? Why?

What is the duty of good government, according to Jonathan Mayhew?

According to Mayhew, when should citizens disobey their government?

If you believed the teachings of Edwards and Mayhew, would you think you had a right—or even a duty—to disobey the king? If so, under what circumstances?

Writing a Diary Entry

Suppose you had lived in one of the 13 colonies in 1750. Write a diary entry about the your experience of the Great Awakening. In your entry, do the following:

- Tell how the sermons of the Great Awakening have affected you.
- Explain whether you feel the same way about people in authority as you did before the Great Awakening, and why or why not.

Use this rubric to evaluate your diary entry. Make changes in your entry if you need to.

Score	Description
3	The diary entry has a clear point of view and many details. It is well constructed as a diary entry. It addresses the points listed. It has no spelling or grammar errors.
2	The diary entry has a clear point of view and some details. It is fairly well constructed as a diary entry. It addresses most of the points listed. It has few spelling or grammar errors.
1	The diary entry does not have a clear point of view and has few details. It is not well constructed as a diary entry. It addresses few of the points listed. It has many spelling or grammar errors.

Timeline Skills

Analyze the Unit 1 timeline in your book. Also think about what you have learned in this unit. Then answer the following questions.

1. About when did the first humans reach the Americas? How did they get there?

2. What was the significance of Magna Carta?

3. About how many American Indians lived north of Mexico in the 1400s? In what ways did American Indian groups differ?

4. When did slavery in the Americas begin?

5. What was the first permanent English colony in the Americas? When was it founded?

6. What document described how the Pilgrims would govern themselves in the Americas?

7. How soon after the founding of Jamestown was the settlement of Providence founded? How soon after the founding of Providence was Pennsylvania founded?

8. What was the significance of the English Bill of Rights?

9. Why were 19 young women executed in Salem, Massachusetts, in 1692?

10. What was the impact of the Great Awakening in the colonies?

Critical Thinking

Use the timeline and the chapters in the unit to answer the following questions.

11. Give two examples of how the environment influenced the cultures of American Indian groups.

12. Would you have preferred to live in Jamestown, Providence, or Pennsylvania? Give at least two reasons for your answer.

13. How did Magna Carta and the English Bill of Rights influence colonists' view of government?

14. If you could add three more events to this timeline, which would they be? List each event, and explain why you think it is important enough to add to the timeline.

    a.

    b.

    c.

Revolution in the Colonies

The Thirteen Colonies

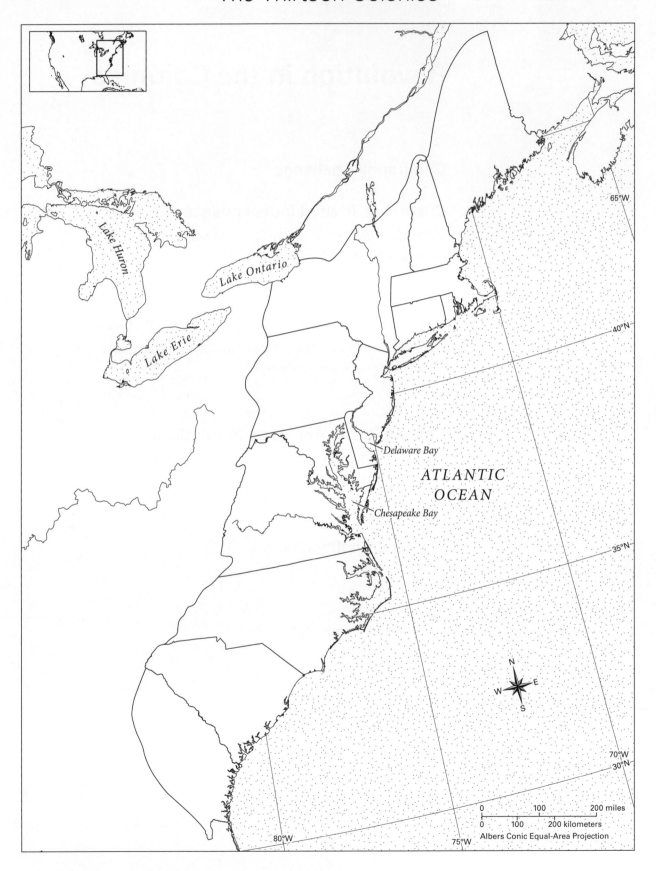

Lake Huron

Lake Ontario

Lake Erie

65°W

40°N

Delaware Bay

ATLANTIC
OCEAN

Chesapeake Bay

35°N

70°W

30°N

N
E
W
S

0   100   200 miles
0   100   200 kilometers
Albers Conic Equal-Area Projection

80°W

75°W

Geography Skills

Analyze the maps in "Setting the Stage" for Unit 2 in your book. Then answer the following questions and fill out the map as directed.

1. Label each colony on the map. Also add and label the colonies' largest cities: Boston, New York, Philadelphia, and Charleston. What do the locations of all four cities have in common?

2. Draw and label the Appalachian Mountains on your map. How many colonists per square mile lived across most of this region?

3. Circle the region where the most colonists lived. What cities does this region include?

4. Shade in the colonies that had large populations of Loyalists. Which of the three main colonial regions had the fewest Loyalists?

5. Based on your map, in which colonies do you predict the goal of independence would have been strongest? Use information from your map to explain why.

6. Label Lake Champlain and the Hudson River. Also add and label Albany. If British armies in Canada and New York City wanted to divide New England from the rest of the colonies, how could they have used the physical geography of this region to carry out this strategy?

Critical Thinking

Answer the following questions in complete sentences.

7. Look at the population density map in your book. How does the amount of settlement along the coast of the 13 colonies compare to the amount of settlement farther inland? What is one possible reason for this?

8. During the first phase of the American Revolution, most major battles took place near the cities of Boston, New York, and Philadelphia. Why would controlling this region have been an important goal for both sides in the war?

9. After years of fighting in the New England and Middle Colonies, British forces invaded Georgia and South Carolina. Based on your map and the maps in your book, why might the British have believed they could conquer this region?

Toward Independence

When is it necessary for citizens to rebel against their government?

PREVIEW

Think about the memo your teacher read from the principal about the new policy to charge students for photocopying. Answer these questions *on a separate sheet of paper.*

1. How did you feel when the memo was read? What were your feelings toward the principal, the volunteer fee collector, and your teacher? Explain.

2. Why did some students decide to pay for photocopying? Why did some not pay?

3. Why did this experience provoke such strong reactions?

READING NOTES

Key Content Terms

As you complete the Reading Notes, use these terms in your answers.

militia   tyranny   repeal   boycott

Section 5.2

1. What powers did colonial governments have in the 18th century?

2. Which event of the French and Indian War do you think was the most significant? Why?

3. Why was the outcome of the war important for American colonists?

1. From 1763 to 1765, British Parliament and King George passed three laws that affected the colonists. Complete the table to explain these events.

Law	What did this law require colonists to do?	How did some colonists protest this law?	How did the British government react to those protests?
Proclamation of 1763		Colonists argued in letters and articles that it was tyranny, an unjust use of government power.	
Stamp Act (1765)	Colonists had to buy a stamp for any paper they used, including news-papers and cards.		
Quartering Act (1765)			

2. What do you think is the best argument for and against each of these laws?

Proclamation of 1763

For:

Against:

Stamp Act

For:

Against:

Quartering Act

For: The soldiers are here to protect the colonies from foreign attack, so colonists should help pay for them!

Against:

1. What were the Townshend Acts? Why did Parliament pass them?

2. Create a drawing or political cartoon to show how the colonists, including Loyalists, reacted to the Townshend Acts. Make sure your illustration shows the influence of colonial women during this action.

3. Explain why Lord North decided to repeal the Townshend Acts in 1770. Then sketch the one item that was left out of the repeal.

1. Draw a Patriot's view and a Loyalist's view of how the Boston Massacre began.

Patriot	Loyalist

2. What role did John Adams play after the Boston Massacre and why?

Section 5.6

1. Rewrite this sentence to make it correct: *The Boston Massacre and the repeal of taxes under the Townshend Acts began huge protests across the colonies.*

2. Give one argument in favor of the Tea Act and one argument against the Tea Act.

3. Write a newspaper headline about the Boston Tea Party from the points of view of a Loyalist and a Patriot. Explain your headlines.

☙ The Loyalist Times ❧	★ The Patriot Press ★

Section 5.7

1. How did King George's feelings toward the colonies change after the Boston Tea Party?

2. Complete the table by recording three actions of the Intolerable Acts. Then take the point of view of a colonist and describe how each action might have hurt you.

Actions of the Intolerable Acts	How might this hurt you?
More soldiers were sent to Boston to make sure colonists followed the laws.	

3. The colonists took several actions to oppose the Intolerable Acts. Which two actions do you agree with the most and why?

4. What new idea did Patrick Henry bring to the First Continental Congress?

5. What decisions did the First Continental Congress make?

Section 5.8

Complete the flowchart of key events of the battles at Lexington and Concord.

> British troops leave Boston and march to Concord to seize gunpowder and weapons.

⬇

>

⬇

> Minutemen and British troops fight in Lexington.

⬇

>

⬇

>

⬇

> Colonists fight British soldiers at Concord's North Bridge.

⬇

>

PROCESSING

Create a pamphlet to persuade colonists to rebel against or remain loyal to the British government. You may choose to express your historical figure's opinion or your own. Fold a sheet of paper into thirds to make your pamphlet. Your pamphlet should have

- an eye-catching title.
- two paragraphs explaining your position for rebellion or loyalty, supported with reasons and examples.
- two or three colorful illustrations.

Preparing to Write: Describing a Hero

With his poem "Paul Revere's Ride," Henry Wadsworth Longfellow made Paul Revere an American hero. Longfellow used words to create his hero. Below is the last verse of the poem. Underline words that might make Paul Revere seem like a hero to readers.

> *So through the night rode Paul Revere;*
> *And so through the night went his cry of alarm*
> *To every Middlesex village and farm—*
> *A cry of defiance and not of fear,*
> *A voice in the darkness, a knock at the door,*
> *And a word that shall echo forevermore!*
> *For borne on the night-wind of the Past,*
> *Through all our history, to the last,*
> *In the hour of darkness and peril and need,*
> *The people will waken and listen to hear*
> *The hurrying hoof-beats of that steed*
> *And the midnight message of Paul Revere.*

What is your definition of a hero?

By your definition, who is someone in your community that you consider to be a hero?

List three reasons why this person is a hero in your eyes.

Write five words or phrases that describe your hero and his or her actions.

Writing a Descriptive Paragraph

Write a clear, descriptive paragraph about your hero. Your paragraph should convince a reader that this person has the qualities of a hero.

Use this rubric to evaluate your paragraph. Make changes in your paragraph if you need to.

Score	Description
3	Paragraph presents convincing detail on heroism. It uses a variety of descriptive words and phrases. It is well constructed with a topic sentence, supporting details, and a conclusion. There are no spelling or grammar errors.
2	Paragraph presents convincing detail on heroism. It uses some descriptive words and phrases. It has a topic sentence, supporting details, and a conclusion. There are some spelling or grammar errors.
1	Paragraph does not present convincing detail on heroism. It has few descriptive words and phrases. It lacks a topic sentence, supporting details, or a conclusion. There are many spelling and grammar errors.

The Declaration of Independence

What principles of government are expressed in the Declaration of Independence?

On a separate sheet of paper, write any phrases or sentences that you know from the Declaration of Independence. In your own words, explain what you think each of these phrases or sentences mean.

Key Content Terms

As you complete the Reading Notes, use these terms in your answers.

independence	*Common Sense*	natural rights
petition	Declaration of Independence	

Section 6.2

1. Who did John Adams propose should be commander-in-chief of the Continental army? What was the main reason he suggested this person?

Events in the Battle of Bunker Hill

2. In the flowchart, record four important details about the Battle of Bunker Hill (Breed's Hill).

3. Sketch the important event that took place in each location. Write a caption for
   each sketch that explains the importance of the event.

Ticonderoga (Winter 1775–1776)   **Boston (March 4, 1776)**

1. Rewrite this sentence to make it correct: *After the battles at Lexington and
   Concord and the British retreat from Boston, there were many more battles,
   and most colonists began to cry for independence.*

2. In the Venn diagram, record at least one similarity and at least three
   differences between the Olive Branch Petition and *Common Sense.*

Olive Branch Petition   ***Common Sense***

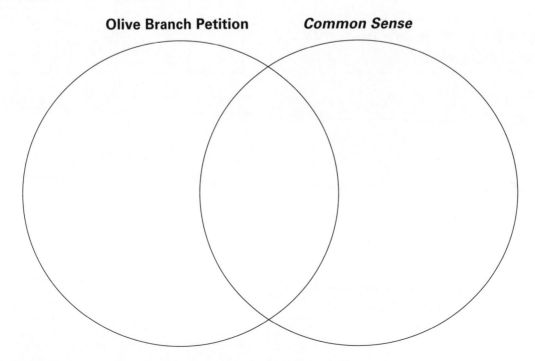

Section 6.4

1. Who drafted the Declaration of Independence? What was his main job in writing this document?

2. Choose three important ideas in the Declaration of Independence. Write them in the chart below. Then explain why you think each idea is important.

Ideas in the Declaration	Why This Idea Is Important
1	
2	
3	

Section 6.5

1. Fill in the thought bubbles. Have each delegate to the Second Continental Congress explain why he opposed Jefferson's passage on slavery.

Northern Delegate   **Southern Delegate**

The Declaration of Independence   **53**

2. Draw a political cartoon that shows what might have happened to the delegates if the new nation had failed to win its freedom from Great Britain. Include a caption explaining your cartoon.

PROCESSING

On another sheet of paper, write a paragraph that explains how one of the following principles of government is expressed in the Declaration of Independence. Support your argument with at least one excerpt from the Declaration.

- Principle 1: All people are created equal.

- Principle 2: All people have basic rights that cannot be taken away.

- Principle 3: The government gets its power to make decisions and to protect rights from the people.

- Principle 4: When the government does not protect the rights of the people, the people have the right to change or remove the government.

Preparing to Write: Identifying a Theme

Common Sense was a best seller from the minute it was published. Historians say that half of all colonists read it or had it read to them. (If a book were published today and half the U.S. population read it, that would be more than 150 million people!)

Suppose you had a chance to publish *Common Sense* today. What would you put on the cover of your pamphlet to entice people to buy it?

Design a front cover for the pamphlet. Include these elements:

- the title
- the author's name
- the date of first publication
- a simple drawing that reflects the pamphlet's theme

Writing Copy for a Cover

Now write the text for the pamphlet's back cover. Include these elements in your copy:

- a two-sentence description of the author
- a paragraph explaining why Paine's ideas seem to be "common sense"

Use this rubric to evaluate your copy for the back cover. Make changes to your copy if you need to.

Score	Description
3	The back cover copy clearly gives all the information. The description is accurate. The paragraph is well written with a topic sentence. There are no spelling or grammar errors.
2	The back cover copy gives most of the information. The description is accurate. The paragraph lacks a topic sentence. There are few spelling or grammar errors.
1	The back cover copy does not give all the information. The description and paragraph are inaccurate. There are many spelling and grammar errors.

The American Revolution

How was the Continental army able to win the war for independence from Great Britain?

PREVIEW

Suppose you were choosing members of a team for the game Capture the Flag. List the three characteristics or skills you think would be most important to look for.

Suppose you have a team of Capture the Flag players who have most of the characteristics and skills you listed above playing against a team with very few of those skills. Which team do you think would win and why?

What other factors might give the team with fewer skills a chance to win?

READING NOTES

Key Content Terms

As you complete the Reading Notes, use these terms in your answers.

American Revolution   Continental army   strategy   ally

1. List at least two strengths and two weaknesses of each side at the start of the war for independence.

American Strengths	British Strengths
American Weaknesses	**British Weaknesses**

2. Complete the sentences for the map of Round 1 of Capture the Flag.

The Blue team is smaller. It has not warmed up. It hasn't played Capture the Flag as much as the Red team, just like

The Red team is larger. It has warmed up. It has played the game more than the Blue team, just like

The Blue captain has experience playing Capture the Flag, just like

The White team cheers for the Blue team, just like

Half the Red team starts the game far from the field, just like

1. Why did the Declaration of Independence increase Americans' motivation to fight and win the war?

2. For which group of Americans did the Declaration of Independence raise hopes as well as questions? Why?

3. What factors allowed the British to almost win the war in 1776?

4. Complete the sentences for the map of Round 2 of Capture the Flag.

The teacher tells the Blue team they will get a prize if they win. This increases their motivation, just like

One Blue player is told he or she might not get a prize, even if the Blue team wins. That player must decide whether to stay on the Blue team or switch to the Red team, just like

Because they have more experienced players, the Red team is almost able to steal the Blue flag, just like

1. In your own words, what was the message of Thomas Paine's pamphlet
   The Crisis?

2. How were the Americans able to win such an overwhelming victory at Trenton?

3. How did victories at Trenton and Princeton affect American morale?

4. Complete the sentences for the map of Round 3 of Capture the Flag.

The teacher gives the Blue team a pep talk and encourages them to keep fighting, just like

The teacher adds a second Blue flag. This makes it harder for the Red team to win and boosts the Blue team's morale, just like

1. As the war progressed, how did General Washington revise his military strategy?

2. Why did the American cause look more hopeful after the Battle of Saratoga?

3. Name two foreigners who were present with the Americans at Valley Forge, and explain how they helped the Americans.

4. Complete the sentences for the map of Round 4 of Capture the Flag.

The teacher tells the Blue team they do not have to capture the Red flag to win. Instead, they must keep the Red team from capturing all the Blue flags, just like

The teacher tells the Blue team that if they can hold on for one more round, they may receive help, just like

The teacher has one volunteer from the White team join the Blue team, just like

1. What tactics did the Americans use successfully against the British in the Southern Colonies?

2. How did the success of the Continental army in the South contribute to the American victory?

3. How did the French help the Americans in the Battle of Yorktown?

4. Complete the sentences for the map of Round 5 of Capture the Flag.

The teacher adds a third Blue flag. This makes it harder for the Red team to win, just like

The White team enters the game to help the Blue team, just like

1. How did the British people and the king respond to news of the Battle of Yorktown?

2. What were three key provisions of the Treaty of Paris?

3. Give two examples of how the American Revolution affected other parts of the world.

4. Complete the sentences for the map of the end of the Capture the Flag game.

Blue flags

We won!

By the end of Round 6, many members of the Red team don't want to play anymore, but some do, just like

At the end of the game, the Blue, White, and Red captains shake hands. The Blue and White teams receive their prizes. The Red captain hands over the Red flag. The Blue team promises to be nice to the Red team, just like

PROCESSING

On a separate piece of paper, create a simile that shows how the Americas were able to beat the British and win the war for independence.

Step 1: Complete this sentence: *The Continental army's victory in the American Revolution was like . . .* Use one of these examples to complete the sentence, or create your own:

- the class game of Capture the Flag
- David's victory over Goliath
- the story of the tortoise and the hare
- a recent sports upset

Step 2: Create a drawing of your simile. Use clever visual details that connect your simile to the Continental army's victory in the American Revolution.

Step 3: Below your drawing, write two "because" statements to explain why your simile is like the Continental army's victory in the American Revolution.

Preparing to Write: Choosing Descriptive Words

For all of his fame, George Washington shared many qualities and emotions that we all have. Write five sentences describing George Washington. Use at least one word from the Word Bank in each sentence.

Word Bank
cautious
compassion
concern
emotional
homesick
proud
strict
uncertain
worried

1.

2.

3.

4.

5.

Writing a Personal Letter

Soldier Joseph Plumb Martin and General George Washington were in the same place a number of times: the Battle of Long Island (1776), Valley Forge (1777–78), the Battle of Monmouth (1778), and the Battle of Yorktown (1781).

At Yorktown, a stranger stopped to talk with Martin and some other soldiers. Martin realized only later that the stranger was the great General Washington. "Had we dared," Martin wrote, "we might have cautioned him for exposing himself so carelessly to danger at such a time."

Suppose you had been Joseph Plumb Martin at Yorktown. What would you like to have told General Washington about your experiences in the war? What emotions would you have shared with him? Express your ideas in a short letter that the soldier might have written to the general. Your letter should clearly describe experiences and emotions related to the war. Be sure to use correct letter format and correct spelling and grammar.

Use this rubric to evaluate your letter. Make changes in your letter if you need to.

Score	Description
3	The letter clearly describes experiences and emotions related to the war. It has correct letter format. There are no spelling or grammar errors.
2	The letter describes experiences and emotions related to the war. It has correct letter format. There are some spelling or grammar errors.
1	The letter does not describe experiences and emotions related to the war. It does not have correct letter format. There are many spelling or grammar errors.

Timeline Skills

Analyze the Unit 2 timeline in your book. Also think about what you have learned in this unit. Then answer the following questions.

1. Which two countries fought each other in the French and Indian War?

2. Why did British Parliament meet with protests from the colonists in the years right after the French and Indian War?

3. What two events occurred in Boston that caused tension between British Parliament and the colonists?

4. When and why did the First Continental Congress meet?

5. What two important documents were published in 1776? Which document could be considered a "cause" and which could be considered an "effect"? Explain.

6. What happened at Lexington and Concord? When did this occur?

7. When and where did the war for independence from Great Britain begin? Did it begin before or after the Declaration of Independence was issued?

8. Why were the Battles of Trenton and Princeton significant? How many years were there between these two battles and the end of the American Revolution?

9. Name one factor that enabled the Continental army to defeat the British army in the revolution.

Critical Thinking

Use the timeline and the chapters in the unit to answer the following questions.

10. Which event that occurred between 1763 and 1776 was the most significant cause of the American Revolution? Explain your opinion.

11. Explain one way the Declaration of Independence continues to guide the nation.

12. What were the most significant factors in the Continental army's victory over the British?

13. If you could add three more events to this timeline, which would they be? List each event, and explain why you think it is important enough to add to the timeline.

    a.

    b.

    c.

Forming a New Nation

The United States, 1790

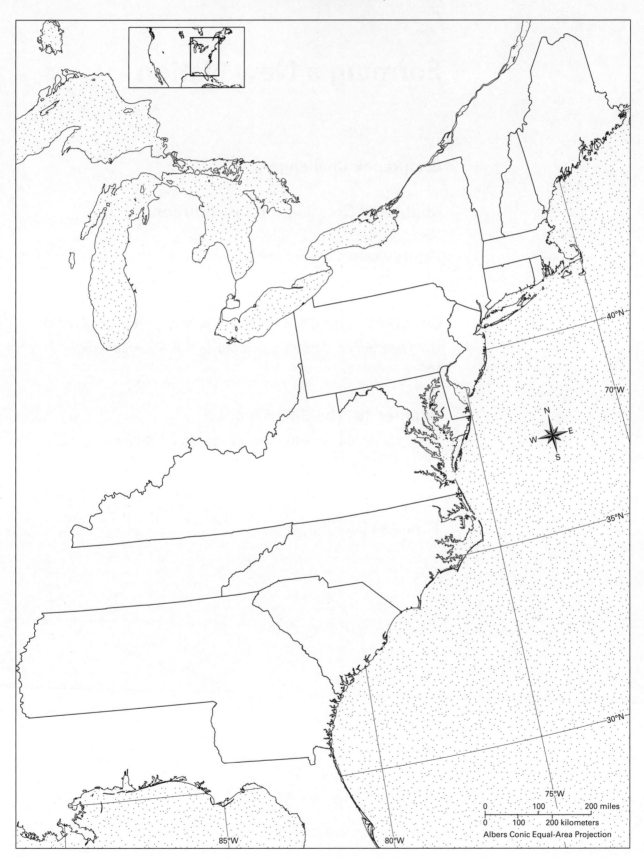

Geography Skills

Analyze the maps in "Setting the Stage" for Unit 3 in your book. Then answer the following questions and fill out the map as directed.

1. Label each state on the map. Which two states had the largest populations?

2. Locate and label the nation's five largest cities in 1790. Which cities are they, and in which state is each located?

3. How many of the nation's 24 largest cities and towns were located in the South?

4. After Charleston and Baltimore, how large were the South's next 4 largest cities? In which state or states were they located?

5. Lightly shade the states where slaves were 20 percent or more of the population. In what region of the nation were most of these states located?

6. Which states had few or no slaves in their populations? In which region of the nation were most of these states located?

7. How many of the nation's 24 largest cities and towns were located in states with few or no slaves in their populations?

8. In which states did slaves count for about one-third or more of the state's population?

9. Circle the names of the Southern states whose population ranks would be affected by a system that did not count slaves as part of a state's population. How would the population rank of each state change?

Critical Thinking
Answer the following questions in complete sentences.

10. Which states would most likely support a system in which the number of votes each state had in the nation's legislature was based on the state's population? Why?

    Which states would probably oppose such a system? Explain why.

11. Why would a state like New Jersey favor a system in which each state had the same number of votes in the nation's legislature?

    What compromise might be found that would be supported by New Jersey as well as by states that wanted the legislature based on the states' populations?

12. Which states would most likely oppose a plan to exclude slaves from a state's population when creating a legislature in which each state's number of votes depended on its population? Which states would most favor such a plan? Explain why.

    Suggest a compromise that both groups of states might support.

Creating the Constitution

What compromises emerged from the Constitutional Convention?

PREVIEW

On a separate sheet of paper, create a T-chart with the heads "Articles of Confederation" and "Classroom Experience." Complete the chart as your class discusses the similarities between what the newly formed United States experienced after the American Revolution and your experience in the classroom.

READING NOTES

Key Content Terms

As you complete the Reading Notes, use these terms in your answers.

Articles of Confederation	Enlightenment	Three-Fifths Compromise
Northwest Territory	republic	Electoral College
Northwest Ordinance	constitution	ratify
Constitutional Convention	Great Compromise	*The Federalist Papers*

Section 8.2

1. What issue did the Land Ordinance of 1785 address?

2. Complete this list of rules for the Northwest Territory.

   Rules Set by the Northwest Ordinance

   • When a territory has 5,000 free adult males, it can elect its own legislature.

   •

   • Settlers have the same rights and privileges as other citizens.

   •

Section 8.3

Fill in the flowchart.

Causes of Shays's Rebellion	Effects of Shays's Rebellion

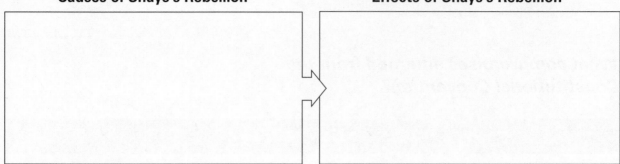

Section 8.4

1. Describe the role of each of these men at the Constitutional Convention.

   George Washington:

   James Madison:

2. Why did the important leaders Sam Adams, John Hancock, and Patrick Henry not attend the convention?

3. Do you agree with the delegates' rule of secrecy? Why or why not?

4. The delegates had differing views on how powerful the national government should be.

   • What did delegates for a strong national government believe?

   • What did delegates for stronger state governments (weaker national government) believe?

   • List one belief that these two types of delegates shared.

1. Tell how each of these would answer this question:
   Where should the government's power to rule come from?

   Articles of Confederation:

   James Madison:

2. Complete the matrix to explain the differences between these two plans of government.

	Virginia Plan	New Jersey Plan
How many branches of government?		
How was the legislature organized?		
Which states did this plan favor? Why?		

1. Who created the plan that became know as the Great Compromise?

2. According to the Great Compromise, how are states represented in each house of Congress?

   In the House of Representatives: In the Senate:

   This favors the (circle one): people states   This favors the (circle one): people states

1. What might each of these delegates have said about how slaves should be counted for representation in Congress?

   Delegate from the North:

   Delegate from the South:

2. Compare the growing division in attitudes toward slavery by writing what each of these delegates might have said.

   Delegate from the North:

   Delegate from the South:

1. How did the Three-Fifths Compromise work? Create and label a simple sketch to illustrate your answer.

2. What compromise did the delegates reach on the slave trade?

1. Fill in the speech bubbles with at least one argument for each proposal.

Delegate Who Believes the Nation Should Have a Single Executive

Delegate Who Believes the Nation Should Have a Three-Member Executive

2. List the three proposals given for choosing the chief executive. Circle the one you think is the best.

1. How many electors does each state have in the Electoral College?

2. Describe one way that presidential elections have changed over time.

Section 8.11

Fill in the speech bubbles to show how each of these delegates might have answered a reporter who asked, "Did you sign the Constitution? Why or why not?"

Benjamin Franklin

George Mason

Elbridge Gerry

Write a one-paragraph letter to the editor of a newspaper from the perspective of a Federalist supporting ratification of the Constitution. Also write a one-paragraph letter to the editor opposing ratification as an Anti-Federalist.

I support ratification because . . .

I do not support ratification because . . .

PROCESSING

On a separate piece of paper, create a poster that might have been used to encourage people to support ratification of the Constitution. Your poster must have

- a catchy slogan.
- three reasons why states should ratify the Constitution.
- an illustration to accompany each reason.
- creative touches to make your poster visually appealing, such as a decorative border.
- writing that uses correct spelling and grammar.

Preparing to Write: Taking Notes

Whether for newspaper, television, radio, or the latest blog, reporters always want to capture "the big story." Newspapers were important in 1787, too. News of the Constitution was announced in papers in all 13 states.

Suppose you were a newspaper reporter on September 17, 1787. The Constitution has just been signed. Your assignment is to write an article about the new Constitution and the convention that created it. In the article, you will describe the event and important issues that were discussed.

Reporters begin by making notes. Use what you have learned about the convention to complete this reporter's notebook. Write down a question you would like to ask three of the delegates. Record what you think they would have replied.

Notes on the Constitutional Convention

What (was the event):

Where (did it happen):

When (did it happen):

Who (was there):

Why (was it happening):

Interviews

My question:

Delegate 1:
Answer:

Delegate 2:
Answer:

Delegate 3:
Answer:

Writing a Newspaper Article

Write your newspaper article below. Your article should clearly report events and issues of the convention and have no spelling or grammar errors. The interviews should give accurate information and opinions. Be sure to give your article a headline, a byline (your name as the reporter), and a dateline (the location and date of the article—in this case, Philadelphia, September 17, 1787).

Use this rubric to evaluate your article. Make changes in your article if you need to.

Score	Description
3	The article clearly reports events and issues of the convention. The interviews give accurate information and opinions. There are no spelling or grammar errors.
2	The article reports events and issues of the convention. The interviews give some accurate information and opinions. There are few spelling or grammar errors.
1	The article does not report events and issues of the convention. The interviews do not give accurate information and opinions. There are many spelling or grammar errors.

The Constitution: A More Perfect Union

How has the Constitution created "a more perfect Union"?

PREVIEW

Read the quotation and answer the questions that follow.

If men were angels, no government would be necessary.

—James Madison

1. In your own words, what is Madison saying?

2. According to Madison, why are governments necessary?

3. Do you agree with Madison? Why or why not?

READING NOTES

Key Content Terms

As you complete the Reading Notes, use these terms in your answers.

popular sovereignty	judicial review	majority rule
legislative branch	checks and balances	interest group
executive branch	interstate commerce	
judicial branch	federalism	

Section 9.2

Read the Preamble to the Constitution below. In your own words, briefly explain what the framers meant by each phrase listed in the chart. An example is done for you.

> *We the People of the United States, in Order to form a more perfect Union, establish Justice, insure domestic Tranquility, provide for the common defence, promote the general Welfare, and secure the Blessings of Liberty to ourselves and our Posterity, do ordain and establish this Constitution for the United States of America.*

"We the People"   The Constitution bases its authority on the people.

"form a more perfect Union"

"establish Justice"

"insure domestic Tranquility"

"provide for the common defence"

"promote the general Welfare"

"secure the Blessings of Liberty"

For each of Sections 9.3 to 9.5, draw a simple illustration at the top of the column to represent that branch of government. Then complete the column.

	9.3 Legislative Branch		9.4 Executive Branch	9.5 Judicial Branch
	Congress House	Senate	Office of the President	Supreme Court
Number of Members				
Length of Term				
Are members elected or appointed?				
Age Requirement				
Citizenship Requirement				
Two or More Powers of This Branch of Government				

1. Why did the framers develop a system of checks and balances?

2. Complete the diagram by writing each of the following checks and balances in the correct arrow.
   - Congress can impeach the president.
   - President calls special sessions of Congress.
   - Supreme Court can declare executive actions unconstitutional.
   - President nominates Supreme Court justices.
   - Congress can override vetoes.
   - Congress can impeach federal judges.
   - Congress approves Supreme Court justices.

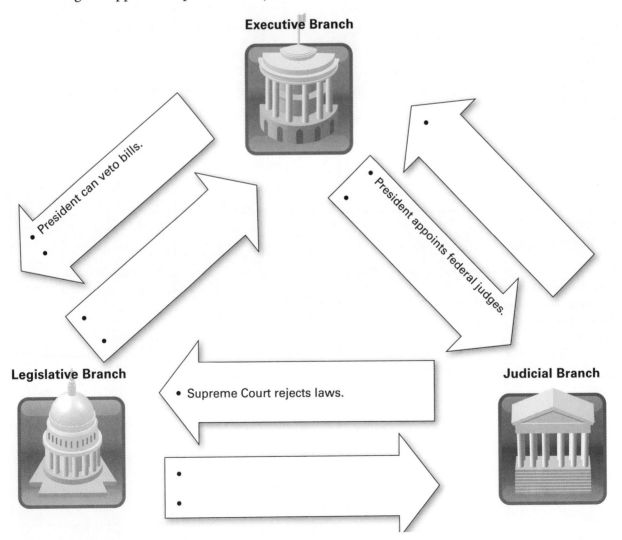

Section 9.7

1. Why did the framers make it possible to change the Constitution but difficult to do so?

2. Create a simple flowchart showing one way that a constitutional amendment can be proposed and ratified.

Section 9.8

1. Why did the framers establish a federal system of government for the United States?

2. What power does the commerce clause give the national government?

3. What advantages were there to having the states share a common market?

1. Describe the principle of majority rule.

2. Create and label drawings that show two ways people can participate in government.

PROCESSING

On a separate sheet of paper, write a letter to James Madison telling him how and why the Constitution has created "a more perfect Union." Your letter must

- include these terms: *popular sovereignty, checks and balances, federalism, majority rule.*
- contain an introductory paragraph telling James Madison the purpose of your letter.
- include at least two additional paragraphs with convincing examples and evidence of how the Constitution has created a more perfect union.
- contain a simple conclusion in which you summarize your main points.
- be free of grammatical and spelling errors.

Preparing to Write: Analyzing a Primary Source Letter

Abigail Adams supported women's rights by words and example. She showed the world that women could be educated, manage a farm, run the home of a president, and more.

In a letter to her husband, John Adams, on March 31, 1776, she urged him to "remember the ladies." Later, on May 7, she wrote,

> I cannot say that I think you are very generous to the ladies; for, whilst you are proclaiming peace and good-will to men, emancipating [freeing] all nations, you insist upon retaining an absolute power over wives.
>
> But you must remember that . . . notwithstanding all your wise laws and maxims [sayings], we have it in our power, not only to free ourselves, but to subdue our masters, and without violence, throw both your natural and legal authority at our feet.

What did Abigail Adams caution her husband against doing?

What did Adams say women had the power to do?

Writing a Letter to the Editor

Suppose you were a woman or a man living in the late 1700s. You agree with Abigail Adams, and you want to promote women's rights. Write a strong letter to the editor of a local newspaper. Try to persuade people to adopt your views.

In your letter, be sure to state a well-defined thesis. (This is your position statement, a clear and knowledgeable proposal.) Support your thesis with detailed examples and sound reasoning. Use correct letter format, spelling, and grammar.

Use this rubric to evaluate your letter. Make changes in your letter if you need to.

Score	Description
3	The letter has a strong thesis and supporting details. It is written in correct letter format. There are no spelling or grammar errors.
2	The letter has a thesis and some supporting details. It is written in letter format. There are few spelling or grammar errors.
1	The letter does not have a thesis or supporting details. It is not written in letter format. There are many spelling or grammar errors.

The Bill of Rights

What rights and freedoms does the Bill of Rights protect and why are they important?

Carefully read the Parents' Constitution. Then answer these questions *on another sheet of paper.* Be prepared to share your answers.

1. Do you believe that parents should have all of the powers described in the Parents' Constitution? Why or why not?

2. List four rights that you would add as amendments to the Parents' Constitution to make it fairer for children and protect them from the power of parents.

3. What parallels can you draw between how you feel about the Parents' Constitution and concerns some people might have felt about the U.S. Constitution when it was first ratified in 1789?

Parents' Constitution

We, the Parents of the United States, in order to form more perfect Families, raise obedient Children, ensure domestic Tranquility, provide for our children's Defense, promote the general Welfare, and secure the Blessings of Liberty to Ourselves and our Children, do ordain and establish this Parents' Constitution for the United States of America.

I. Parents shall have the power to command complete respect from their children.

II. Parents shall have the power to assign chores to their children.

III. Parents shall have the power to promote family togetherness even if this power interferes with their children's social lives.

IV. Parents shall have the power to ask their children questions and to expect honest answers.

V. Parents shall have the power to make all decisions about family spending, including the power to restrict children's spending on unproductive or harmful items.

VI. Parents shall have the power to decide how much time their children's friends can spend with their children.

READING NOTES

Key Content Terms

As you complete the Reading Notes, use these terms in your answers.

Bill of Rights	double jeopardy	due process
warrant	self-incrimination	defendant

Section 10.2

1. What does the Bill of Rights contain?

2. Who took the lead in making sure the Bill of Rights was eventually included in the Constitution?

Section 10.3

1. List the five basic freedoms protected by the First Amendment. Put a check next to each of those freedoms that you exercise in your daily life. Then select one of your checked freedoms and briefly explain why it is important to you.

2. Create a simple drawing with labels that represents Thomas Jefferson's view of the relationship between religion (church) and government (state).

3. Not all of the founders agreed with Jefferson's view on the separation of church and state. Do you agree with Jefferson or with his opponents? Explain.

4. Find an Internet site or newspaper article that is an example of one of the roles the press plays in a democratic society—for example, government watchdog or keeping citizens informed. Tape the article into your notebook or onto a separate sheet of paper. In the space below, briefly explain which role the article is an example of.

5. In the case of *Texas v. Johnson*, the Supreme Court held that freedom of speech means more than just words. Cite an example of symbolic speech. Do you agree that the First Amendment should protect this kind of symbolic speech? Why or why not?

Section 10.4

1. List the two basic rights protected by the Second and Third Amendments.

2. Some people argue that the Second and Third Amendments are not particularly relevant in today's society. Do you agree? Why or why not?

3. What steps must the police follow to search someone or someone's property? Create a simple flowchart to show your answer.

Section 10.5

1. List and describe five important rights protected by the Fifth Amendment. Then circle one of these rights and briefly explain why you think it is important.

2. To the spoke diagram below, add and label at least four spokes for key rights protected by the Sixth Amendment, such as the right to a speedy trial. Draw a symbol for each right. Finally, highlight the right that you think is most important and briefly explain why.

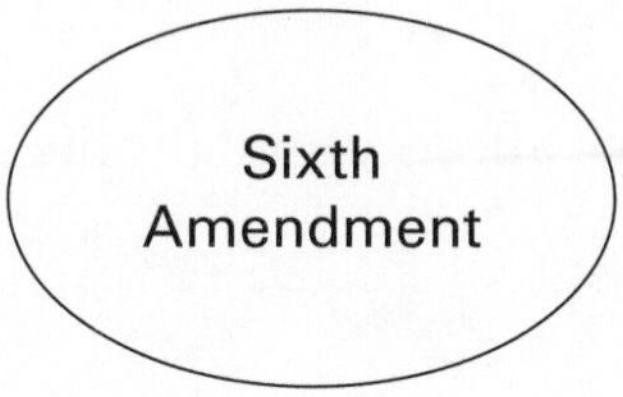

Sixth
Amendment

3. The Eighth Amendment protects an accused person's rights before and after a trial. Create a simple political cartoon, with speech bubbles or captions, that shows one of the rights protected by the Eighth Amendment and why it is important.

Section 10.6

1. According to the Ninth Amendment, who retains rights not specifically listed in the Constitution?

2. What is one example of a reserved power that affects your daily life?

PROCESSING

Select one of the ten amendments in the Bill of Rights you think is most important or has the greatest impact on your daily life. *On a separate sheet of paper,* write a personal narrative describing what a day in your life might be like without the rights and freedoms that particular amendment protects. Your narrative should include

- an interesting title that clearly identifies which amendment the narrative is about, such as "Life Without the Fourth Amendment."

- at least two incidents or situations that could occur in your daily life if you did not have the rights or freedoms protected by that amendment. Describe the situations clearly and use well-chosen, interesting details.

- relevant dialogue. For example: "I have the right!" I said. "Actually, you don't," replied the judge.

- a clear argument about why it is important to have this amendment in the Bill of Rights. As part of your argument, reflect on the significance of the situations you have described.

- a photograph or drawing representing an important part of your narrative.

Preparing to Write: Analyzing Legal Language

Thomas Jefferson believed that church and state—religion and government—should be separate. Both institutions would be healthier that way, he said. In his view, a "wall of separation" was the only true way to preserve religious freedom.

Jefferson wrote the Statute for Religious Freedom, a law that the Virginia legislature passed in 1786. This law became a model for legislation on religious freedom. The sentence below is at the heart of the statute. It is a long, wordy sentence, like much legal language then—and now. To better understand a sentence like this, it helps to break it into smaller parts.

After each part of the sentence, write a simple explanation that your friends could understand. Use a dictionary to help you.

Be it enacted by the General Assembly [of Virginia], That no man shall be compelled to frequent [attend] or support any religious worship, place, or ministry whatsoever,

nor shall be enforced, restrained, molested, or burthened [burdened] in his body or goods, nor shall otherwise suffer on account of his religious opinions or belief;

but that all men shall be free to profess, and by argument to maintain, their opinions in matters of Religion,

and that the same shall in no wise [way] diminish, enlarge or affect their civil capacities [civil rights].

Writing a Statute

Thomas Jefferson wrote the Statute for Religious Freedom because he believed that religious freedom was one of the "natural rights of mankind."

Think about a right that you believe in and would like to see incorporated into your school's rules. Write a "statute" that would make this right part of the school rules. Your statute should describe the right clearly. It should indicate what behaviors the right would prohibit or allow. And it should tell why you believe that students should have this right.

Use this rubric to evaluate your statute. Make changes in your statute if you need to.

Score	Description
3	The statute clearly states a right. It describes appropriate behaviors. It gives good reasons to justify the right. There are no spelling or grammar errors.
2	The statute states a right. It describes some appropriate behaviors. It gives some reasons to justify the right. There are few spelling or grammar errors.
1	The statute does not clearly state a right. It does not describe appropriate behaviors. It does not justify the right. There are many spelling or grammar errors.

Timeline Skills

Analyze the Unit 3 timeline in your book. Also think about what you have learned in this unit. Then answer the following questions.

1. Which plan of government was in place in the United States during Shays's Rebellion?

2. How did the Northwest Ordinance relate to the Northwest Territory?

3. George Washington was selected to preside over which of the events on the timeline?

4. James Madison, Alexander Hamilton, and John Jay were the authors of which item on the timeline?

5. How many years passed between adoption of the U.S. Constitution and the ratification of the Bill of Rights?

6. The principle of freedom of speech most closely relates to which item on the timeline?

Critical Thinking

Use the timeline and the chapters in the unit to answer the following questions.

7. Explain how the Articles of Confederation helped lead to Shays's Rebellion.

8. Besides the Great Compromise, describe another important compromise that was reached during the Constitutional Convention.

9. Explain how *The Federalist Papers* influenced one of the other timeline items that happened close to the same time.

10. If you could add two more events to this timeline, which would they be? List each event, and explain why you think it is important enough to add to the timeline.

    a.

    b.

Launching the New Republic

Geography Challenge

Chapter 11: Political Developments in the Early Republic

How did the Federalist and Republican visions for the United States differ?

Chapter 12: Foreign Affairs in the Young Nation

To what extent should the United States have become involved in world affairs in the early 1800s?

Chapter 13: A Growing Sense of Nationhood

What did it mean to be an American in the early 1800s?

Chapter 14: Andrew Jackson and the Growth of American Democracy

How well did President Andrew Jackson promote democracy?

Timeline Challenge

The United States, 1838

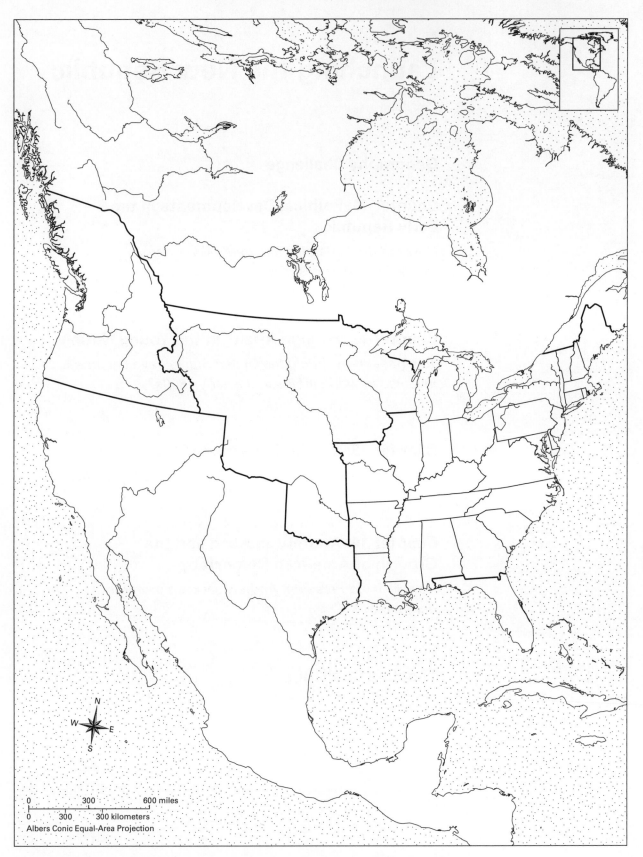

0   300   600 miles
0   300   300 kilometers
Albers Conic Equal-Area Projection

Geography Skills

Analyze the map and graph in "Setting the Stage" for Unit 4 in your book. Then answer the following questions and fill out the map as directed.

1. Label each of the states on your map. By how many states had the nation grown from 1791 to 1838?

2. During which decade—the 1790s, 1800s, 1810s, 1820s, or 1830s—were the most states admitted to the Union? Identify those states on your map by circling their labels.

3. Which is the only new state added to the Union in the early 1800s that is not located west of the Appalachian Mountains? Name it here, and shade it on your map.

4. Where was the nation's capital located when George Washington became the first president? Locate and label it.

5. Locate and label Baltimore and New Orleans. What happened in these cities that shows that the young United States had problems in its relations with other nations?

    With which nation did the United States have a problem in this situation?

6. Draw and label the Erie Canal. Which two bodies of water did it connect? Name them here, and label them on your map.

7. Locate the home state of President Andrew Jackson on your map. Name it here.

8. Draw and label the general route of the Trail of Tears on your map. What took place along this route? Where did the trail begin and where did it end?

Critical Thinking
Answer the following questions in complete sentences.

9. What effect might a foreign conflict like the one mentioned in the reading have on Americans' support for their new nation and its government?

10. How does the election of President Andrew Jackson illustrate the nation's westward growth? How might that growth have made Jackson's election possible?

11. For what reason might the U.S. government have forced the Cherokee to give up their land and move west? Do you think this change was progress for the nation? Explain why or why not.

Political Developments in the Early Republic

How did the Federalist and Republican visions for the United States differ?

PREVIEW

Listen to the songs "Hail, Columbia" and "Fair and Free Elections." Then answer these questions *on another piece of paper.*

Hail, Columbia

1. What are three adjectives that describe the song's mood?

2. How do you think Washington's swearing in as president united the country?

Fair and Free Elections

1. What are three adjectives that describe the song's mood?

2. According to the lyrics, what were some of the issues of the 1800 presidential election?

3. In what ways do you think the nation changed between Washington's inauguration in 1789 and the election of 1800?

READING NOTES

Key Content Terms

As you complete the Reading Notes, use these terms in your answers.

Whiskey Rebellion	sedition
Washington's Farewell Address	nullify
loose construction	states' rights theory
strict construction	

Section 11.2

1. What issue divided the first Congress as the nation launched the new government?

2. Complete the spoke diagram illustrating the nation's first executive branch under George Washington. Draw a symbol to represent each department. Then, on the spokes, list the role of each department and the person who headed it.

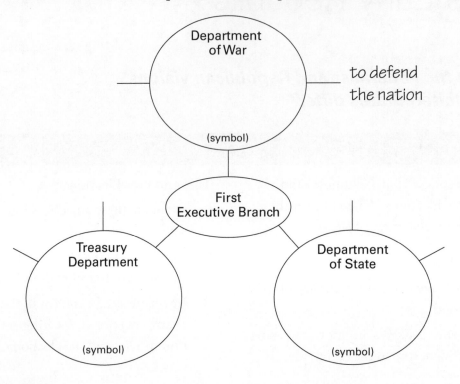

Department
of War

to defend
the nation

(symbol)

First
Executive Branch

Treasury
Department

Department
of State

(symbol)

(symbol)

Section 11.3

1. Create a simple illustration showing the government's response to the Whiskey Rebellion. Also explain whether you think the government acted appropriately.

2. Explain in your own words what Washington in his Farewell Address meant by the threat of the "spirit of party."

Sections 11.4 and 11.5

Read Section 11.4 and write a response to Questions 1 to 6 from the perspective of Alexander Hamilton. Then read Section 11.5 and write responses to the questions from the perspective of Thomas Jefferson.

1. What is your view of human nature?

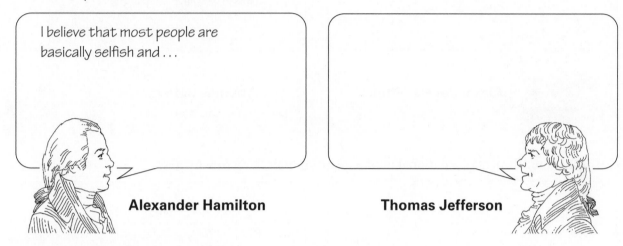

I believe that most people are basically selfish and . . .

Alexander Hamilton   **Thomas Jefferson**

2. Who should lead our country?

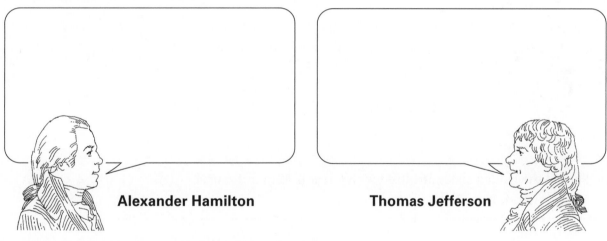

Alexander Hamilton   **Thomas Jefferson**

3. How strong should our national government be?

Alexander Hamilton   **Thomas Jefferson**

4. What is the ideal economy?

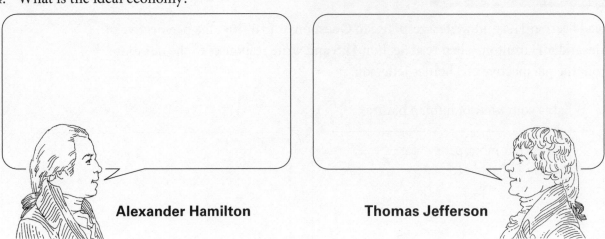

Alexander Hamilton

Thomas Jefferson

5. Is the establishment of a national bank constitutional? Why or why not?

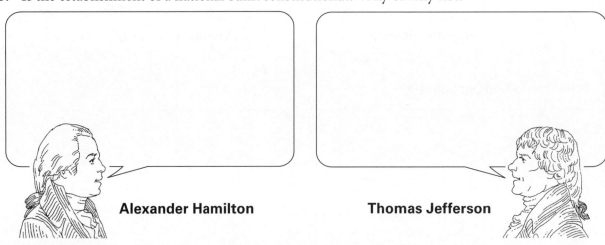

Alexander Hamilton

Thomas Jefferson

6. Should the United States ally itself with Great Britain or France?
Why or why not?

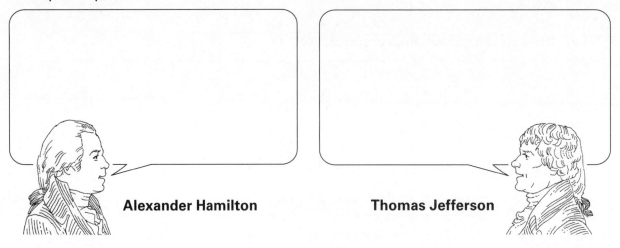

Alexander Hamilton

Thomas Jefferson

Section 11.6

Complete the poster, which urges state legislatures to nullify the Alien and Sedition Acts. Include at least two reasons for nullification and one illustration on your poster.

Nullify the Alien and Sedition Acts!

Section 11.7

In the banners, write two campaign slogans for the 1800 presidential election—
one from the perspective of a Federalist and one from the perspective of a Republican.
Include the name of the candidate and a reason he should be elected. For example:
A strong foreign policy is what we need! With John Adams as president, we will succeed!

Republican Party

Federalist Party

1. Why was the Twelfth Amendment added to the Constitution?

2. What does the Twelfth Amendment prevent?

PROCESSING

Suppose you are the campaign manager for one of the presidential candidates in 1800. *On a separate piece of paper,* create a campaign song for your candidate. Your song can be to the tune of "Hail, Columbia," "Fair and Free Elections," or any other tune you choose. Your song must

- clearly describe the Federalist or the Republican vision for the United States.
- contain at least two reasons why your candidate should be elected.
- use language that reflects the passionate feelings held by Federalists or Republicans.

Preparing to Write: Translating Visual Ideas into Words

Today, we think of the White House as a symbol of the presidency. But it has not always looked just as it does today. In fact, if Thomas Jefferson had had his way, it would have looked very different.

How did Thomas Jefferson's ideas about how the president's house should look reflect his ideas about the presidency?

How did George Washington's ideas about how the president's house should look reflect his ideas about the presidency?

If you were designing a house for the president today, what would it look like? Think about how your design would reflect your ideas about the presidency. Use the space below to make notes and sketches for your design.

Writing About a Design

Suppose you entered a national contest to design a new house for the president. Write a paragraph describing your house design. Discuss the reasons why you designed it as you did. Also explain how your design reflects your ideas about the presidency. You may wish to make a floor plan of the house on another sheet of paper. Make sure your descriptions and explanations are free of spelling and grammar errors.

Use this rubric to evaluate your contest entry. Make changes in your entry if you need to.

Score	Description
3	The paragraph gives a clear description of and explanation for the design. There are no spelling or grammar errors.
2	The paragraph gives a description of and explanation for the design. There are few spelling or grammar errors.
1	The paragraph does not give a clear description of or explanation for the design. There are many spelling or grammar errors.

Foreign Affairs in the Young Nation

To what extent should the United States have become involved in world affairs in the early 1800s?

PREVIEW

Examine the map your teacher has projected, or look at the map in Section 12.2 of your book. Then answer these questions *on another sheet of paper.*

1. What does this map show?

2. What countries might have posed a potential threat to the United States in 1796?

3. What geographic advantages did the United States have in a potential attack? What geographic disadvantages did it have?

4. Suppose that it is 1796. Do you think the United States should become involved in world affairs? Why or why not?

READING NOTES

Key Content Terms

As you complete the Reading Notes, use these terms in your answers.

neutrality	embargo	Monroe Doctrine
isolationism	blockade	

Section 12.2

1. Complete the diagram to show foreign threats to the United States in 1789.

Unfriendly neighbors surrounded the country.

(Foreign Threats in 1789)

2. Suppose George Washington has just given his Farewell Address. Complete the statement to explain the foreign policy he thinks the United States should pursue.

I have declared a policy of neutrality and isolationism. This means

1. What did the Jay Treaty resolve? How did the French respond to the treaty?

2. Draw and label a simple illustration to represent the XYZ Affair. Then describe how Congress reacted to the incident.

1. Describe what President Adams did to protect U.S. ships in the Atlantic. Then explain whether you think he pursued the best foreign policy option.

2. Mark an **X** along the spectrum to indicate where President Adams's response to attacks on U.S. ships falls. Then write a sentence explaining your placement.

Isolationism   Total Involvement

Section 12.5

1. Why did Great Britain impress U.S. sailors in the early 1800s?

2. Create a simple drawing to represent the problem of piracy by the Barbary States of North Africa. Then explain President Jefferson's dilemma.

Section 12.6

1. Describe how President Jefferson responded to piracy in the Mediterranean and to the continued seizures of ships by the British and French. Then explain whether you think he pursued the best foreign policy options.

2. Mark an **X** along the spectrum to indicate where President Jefferson's response to piracy in the Mediterranean falls. Mark an O to indicate whether his response to seizures of U.S. ships by Great Britain and France reflected more isolationism or more involvement. Then write a sentence explaining your placements.

Isolationism   Total Involvement

Complete the diagram to show the reasons why many Americans wanted to go to war with Great Britain in early 1812.

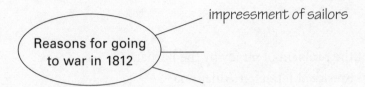

Reasons for going to war in 1812

impressment of sailors

1. Complete the timeline of the War of 1812. For each month marked, briefly describe the event that happened and create a symbol to represent it.

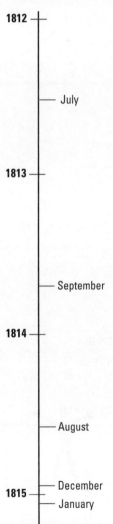

1812

— July

1813

— September

1814

— August

— December
1815
— January

2. Mark an **X** along the spectrum to indicate where President Madison's decision to declare war on Great Britain falls. Then write a sentence justifying your placement.

Isolationism   Total Involvement

Section 12.9

Why might the United States have been interested in supporting the new Latin American nations in the early 1800s?

Section 12.10

1. In your own words, explain what the Monroe Doctrine said. Then explain whether you think President Monroe pursued the best foreign policy option.

2. Mark an **X** along the spectrum to indicate where the Monroe Doctrine falls.
    Then write a sentence explaining your placement.

Isolationism   Total Involvement

John Adams was so proud of avoiding war with France that he wanted that
fact engraved on his tombstone. *On a separate sheet of paper,* create a tombstone
like the one below for each of these presidents:

George Washington (1732–1799)

John Adams (1735–1826)

Thomas Jefferson (1743–1826)

James Madison (1751–1836)

James Monroe (1758–1831)

John Adams

1735–1826

*He avoided war
with France.*

*He should have
been more involved
in world affairs
because . . .*

Each tombstone should include
- the years the president lived.
- one example of how the president became involved in foreign affairs.
- one sentence explaining to what extent you think the president should
  have been involved in world affairs.
- a symbol representing the president's foreign policy decisions.

Preparing to Write: Analyzing Motives

"This Land Is Your Land" is a famous song by American folk singer Woody Guthrie. One line says that the land—the physical United States—was made for you and for me. Just who owns the land has been an ongoing question in our nation's history. The Shawnee leader Tecumseh challenged both American Indians and the U.S. government on land ownership.

According to Tecumseh, why should a tribe not sell land?

Why did Tecumseh want to unite American Indian tribes?

Why did Tecumseh refuse to retreat at the Battle of the Thames?

Writing About Points of View

White settlers and the U.S. government believed they had a right to buy land from American Indians. Tecumseh and his followers argued that the Indians did not have the right to sell the land. The two groups had different points of view. On the next page, you will write a statement about each point of view. Make sure your statements are free of spelling and grammar errors.

Write a short statement explaining the point of view of a white settler. Give supporting details for this point of view.

Write another statement explaining the point of view of a follower of Tecumseh. Give supporting details for this point of view.

Use this rubric to evaluate your statements. Make changes in your statements if you need to.

Score	Description
3	The statements have a clear point of view and supporting details. There are no spelling or grammar errors.
2	The statements have a point of view and some supporting details. There are some spelling or grammar errors.
1	The statements do not have a clear point of view or many details. There are many spelling or grammar errors.

A Growing Sense of Nationhood

What did it mean to be an American in the early 1800s?

PREVIEW

Read the lyrics below. *On a separate piece of paper*, answer the questions that follow.

The Star-Spangled Banner

O say can you see, by the dawn's early light,

What so proudly we hailed at the twilight's last gleaming?

Whose broad stripes and bright stars, through the perilous fight,

O'er the ramparts we watched, were so gallantly streaming?

And the rockets' red glare, the bombs bursting in air,

Gave proof through the night that our flag was still there.

O say does that star-spangled banner yet wave

O'er the land of the free and the home of the brave?

1. How does the song make you feel? Provide three adjectives.
2. What story does the song tell?
3. What does the song tell us about what it meant to be an American in the early 1800s?

READING NOTES

Key Content Terms

As you complete the Reading Notes, use these terms in your answers.

frontier	folk art
capitalism	spiritual
American System	

Section 13.2

1. Describe three characteristics of life in the early 1800s.

2. Create an illustration that highlights an American symbol or value of the period. For example, you might draw a frontier settler in the wilderness to represent individualism. Write a sentence explaining your illustration.

Section 13.3

1. Complete the spoke diagram showing the main components of Henry Clay's American System.

Federal spending on transportation projects

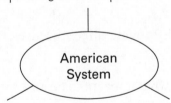

American System

2. Give an example of how decisions by the Supreme Court, under Chief Justice John Marshall, strengthened federal power.

If your class is doing the activity for this chapter, complete the entire matrix below.
(Note: If your class is not doing the activity, fill in only the first two columns.)

Read Section 13.4 and complete the second and third columns of the matrix. Then, as you visit each placard, determine which style or artist the placard relates to, and fill in the remaining information for that row.

Early 1800s Style or Artist	Two Characteristics of This Style or Artist	Draw a Symbol to Represent This Style or Artist	Placard Letter and Why You Chose It	What Makes This Piece American
Folk Art				
Portraits				
Hudson River School				
John James Audubon				
George Catlin				

1. Complete the spoke diagram of popular early American music. In the ovals, list the four types of music described in the section. (One is given for you.) On each spoke, write a characteristic of that type of music.

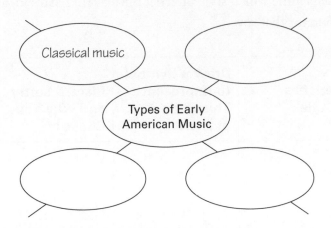

Classical music

Types of Early American Music

2. Use information from Section 13.5 to describe what this painting shows.

If your class is doing the activity for this chapter, complete the entire matrix below.
(Note: If your class is not doing the activity, fill in only the first two columns.)

As you read Section 13.6, complete the second and third columns of the matrix. Then read each literature excerpt with your group to determine its author, and record your answer. Finally, complete the last column.

Early 1800s Author	One Work by the Author	One Characteristic of Author's Works	Matching Excerpt Letter and Why You Chose It	What Makes This Excerpt American
Washington Irving				
James Fenimore Cooper				
Davy Crockett				
Henry Wadsworth Longfellow				

Read part of the short story "Bear Hunting in Tennessee" by Davy Crockett.

In the fall of 1825, I concluded I would build two large boats, and load them with pipe staves [narrow strips of wood] for market. So I went down to the lake, which was about twenty-five miles from where I lived, and hired some hands [workers] to assist me, and went to work; some at boat building, and others to getting staves. I worked on with my hands till the bears got fat, and then I turned out to hunting, to lay in a supply of meat. I soon killed and salted down as many as were necessary for my family; but about this time one of my old neighbours, who had settled down on the lake about twenty-five miles from me, came to my house and told me he wanted me to go down and kill some bears about in his parts. He said they were extremely fat, and very plenty. I know'd that when they were fat, they were easily taken, for a fat bear can't run fast or long. But I asked a bear no favours, no way, further than civility [politeness], for I now had eight large dogs . . . so that a bear stood no chance at all to get away from them. So I went home with him, and then went on down towards the Mississippi, and commenced hunting.

Writing from the perspective of Davy Crockett, complete this short story about hunting bears. Do your writing *on another sheet of paper*. Remember that Crockett tended to exaggerate to make his stories more entertaining. Your story should bring out details of what it meant to be an American living on the frontier.

Your piece should be at least two paragraphs long and free of spelling and grammatical errors. It should also include

- at least three details describing frontier life.

- a statement on what it means to be an American in the early 1800s.

Preparing to Write: Analyzing Characters in Literature

Rip Van Winkle and Natty Bumppo are famous characters in American literature. Washington Irving and James Fenimore Cooper created them to show a time of change in the young United States.

Adjectives are an important component of an author's toolkit for creating a character. List four adjectives that describe Rip Van Winkle.

What was changing in Rip Van Winkle's world?

In a story or novel, the author puts characters in situations that make a point. What point did Cooper want to make in the scene of settlers shooting pigeons?

What was changing in Natty Bumppo's world?

Writing a Character Description

Suppose you wanted to write a story about change in the United States today. For example, how is technology changing our lives? How is the environment changing? Describe the changes you would like to write about.

Create a character to include in your story. Write a description of your character.

Describe one situation you would create for your character. It should make a point about change.

Use this rubric to evaluate your descriptions. Make changes in them if you need to.

Score	Description
3	The descriptions give clear details. The situation makes a clear point about change. There are no spelling or grammar errors.
2	The descriptions give some details. The situation makes a point about change. There are some spelling or grammar errors.
1	The descriptions do not give details. The situation does not make a point about change. There are many spelling or grammar errors.

Andrew Jackson and the Growth of American Democracy

How well did President Andrew Jackson promote democracy?

PREVIEW

Follow along with the lyrics as you listen to this folk song, which was written in 1821 by Samuel Woodworth.

The Hunters of Kentucky

Hail gentlemen and ladies fair,
That grace this famous city,
Come listen, if you've time to spare
While I rehearse this ditty.
And for the opportunity
Consider yourself lucky,
It is not often that you see
A hunter from Kentucky.

Now, you all did read in the public prints
How Pakenham [English general] attempted
To make our Hickory Jackson wince,
As soon his scheme repented.
But Jackson, he was wide awake,
And he wasn't scared of trifles [things of little importance];
Well he knew what aim we'd take
With our Kentucky rifles;

Well, a bank was raised to hide our breast,
Not that we thought of dying,
But that we always like to rest
Unless the game is flying.
Behind it stood our little band,
None wished it to be greater.
Every man was half a horse,
And half an alligator.

Well, the British found 'twas vain to fight,
Where lead was all the booty,
And so they wisely took to flight,
And left us all this beauty.
So, if danger e'er annoys,
Remember what our trade is.
Send for us Kentucky boys,
And we'll protect ye ladies.

Answer these questions *on a separate sheet of paper.*

1. What are two adjectives that describe the song's mood?

2. What story does the song tell?

3. What qualities does the song suggest would make Jackson a good president?

READING NOTES

Key Content Terms

As you complete the Reading Notes, use these terms in your answers.

Jacksonian Democracy   spoils system   secede

civil servant   tariff   Trail of Tears

Section 14.2

1. Complete this road map of Andrew Jackson's journey from the frontier to the White House. In each space, write a sentence explaining the date's significance.

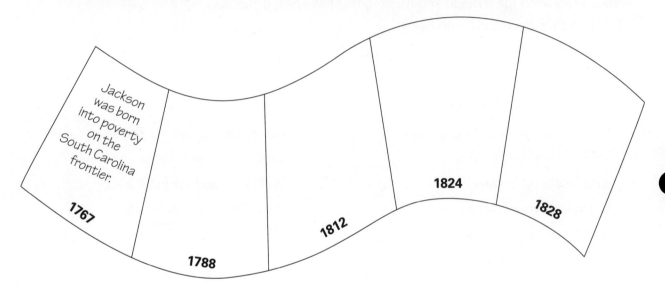

2. Add dialogue in the speech bubbles to reflect what the common people and the upper class might have felt about Jackson's journey from the frontier to the White House. Use these words in your dialogue: *Democratic Party, Jacksonian Democracy.*

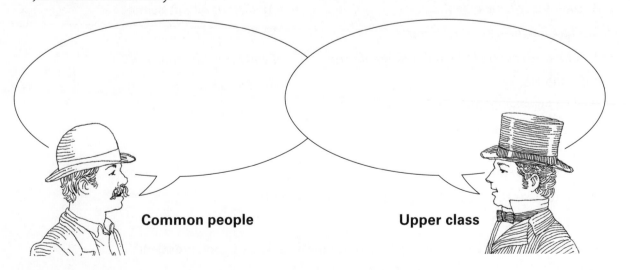

Common people   **Upper class**

        © Teachers' Curriculum Institute

Section 14.3

1. Add dialogue to the speech bubbles to reflect what the common people and the upper class might have felt about Andrew Jackson's inauguration.

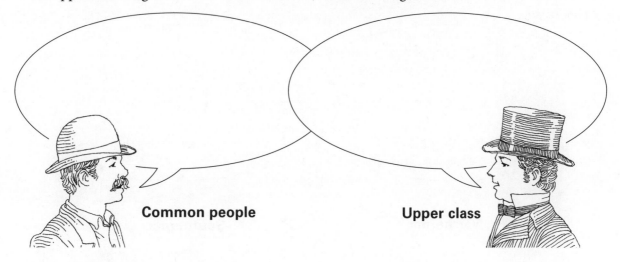

Common people

Upper class

2. What did President Jackson promise he would do to promote democracy?

Section 14.4

1. Add dialogue to the speech bubbles to reflect what the common people and upper class might have felt about Andrew Jackson's approach to governing. Use these words in your dialogue: *civil servants, spoils system*.

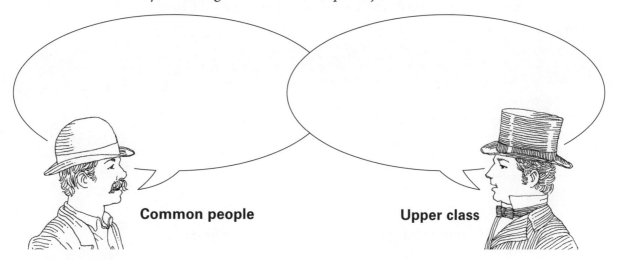

Common people

Upper class

2. Do you think Jackson's approach to governing promoted democracy? Why or why not?

Section 14.5

1. Add dialogue to the speech bubbles to reflect how northerners and southerners might have felt about the new tariff law of 1828. Use these words in your dialogue: *tariff, secede.*

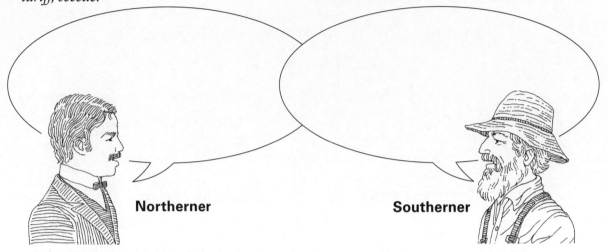

Northerner   Southerner

3. Do you think Jackson's response to the nullification crisis promoted democracy? Why or why not?

Section 14.6

1. Add dialogue to the speech bubbles to reflect how the common people and the upper class might have felt about Andrew Jackson's battle with the Bank of the United States.

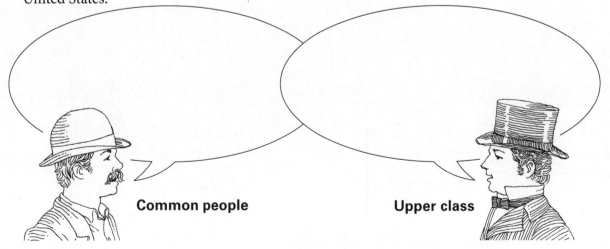

Common people   Upper class

2. Do you think Jackson's dismantling of the bank promoted democracy? Why or why not?

1. Add dialogue to the speech bubble to reflect how American Indians might have felt about Andrew Jackson's Indian policy to remove Indians from the East by force. Include these words in your dialogue: *treaty, Trail of Tears.*

American Indian

2. Do you think Jackson's Indian policy promoted democracy? Why or why not?

PROCESSING

Evaluate how well Andrew Jackson promoted democracy during his presidency. *On a separate sheet of paper,* create a "hero's plaque" for Jackson that highlights his positive contributions to American democracy. On the opposite side, create a "wanted" poster that emphasizes his negative impact on American democracy.

Include the following on your plaque:

• a sketch of Jackson

• two sentences stating why he should be praised

• two symbols that represent him as a hero

Include the following on your poster:

• a sketch of Jackson

• two sentences stating why he should be criticized

• two symbols that represent him as a villain

Then write a paragraph that answers this question: *How well did Andrew Jackson promote democracy?*

Preparing to Write: Understanding Chronology

From early colonial times on, newcomers believed they had the right to claim land wherever American Indians lived. Europeans had been in conflict with the Cherokees since the 1600s, when English colonists came to Virginia. For more than 50 years after the American Revolution, the Cherokee Nation struggled with the more powerful nation in which it existed—the United States.

Place these six sentences about the conflict in chronological order by numbering them from 1 to 6.

____ Congress passed the Indian Removal Act.

____ The Cherokees were allies of the United States in the War of 1812.

____ Some Cherokee leaders signed the Treaty of New Echota.

____ The Cherokees occupied a reduced homeland after the American Revolution.

____ The Cherokees were forced to leave their homeland and go to Indian Territory.

____ Gold was discovered on Cherokee land.

In the conflict between the Cherokees and the United States, what did the Cherokees want to achieve?

What did the U.S. government want to achieve?

Writing a Letter to the Editor

Some Americans were angered by Andrew Jackson's policy of forced removal of American Indians from their lands. Take the position of one such American in 1839. Write a letter to the editor of your local newspaper, protesting the removal of the Cherokees. In your letter, do the following:

- Describe the physical and emotional hardships the Cherokees faced during the removal. Include an eyewitness report.
- Include arguments designed to persuade the president to change his policy.

Use this rubric to evaluate your letter. Make changes in your letter if you need to.

Score	Description
3	The letter has convincing descriptions and arguments. It is well constructed with correct letter format. There are no spelling or grammar errors.
2	The letter has descriptions and arguments. It is constructed with correct letter format. There are some spelling or grammar errors.
1	The letter does not have descriptions or arguments. It is not constructed with correct letter format. There are many spelling or grammar errors.

Timeline Skills

Analyze the Unit 4 timeline in your book. Also think about what you have learned in this unit. Then answer the following questions.

1. For how many years did George Washington serve as president?

2. How many terms did Washington serve? Why is this fact significant?

3. During which president's administration were the Alien and Sedition Acts passed?

4. The Treaty of Paris ended the American Revolution in 1783. How many years passed before the United States was again at war with Great Britain?

5. Why did the United States fight the War of 1812?

6. What message did the Monroe Doctrine send to the world?

7. When did the era of Jacksonian Democracy begin? What did it stand for?

8. How did the federal government implement the Indian Removal Act in 1838?

Critical Thinking

Use the timeline and the chapters in the unit to answer the following questions.

9. The Whiskey Rebellion arose in response to a major problem that faced the new nation. What was this major problem, and how did it arise?

What did the government do to address this problem?

10. Explain at least three key points of difference between the Federalists and the Republicans. Also name one leader of each party.

11. Compare the foreign policy advice of George Washington with the actions of James Madison. What motivated each president?

12. If you could add three more events to this timeline, which would they be? List each event, and explain why you think it is important enough to add to the timeline.

    a.

    b.

    c.

An Expanding Nation

U.S. Territorial Acquisitions, 1803–1853

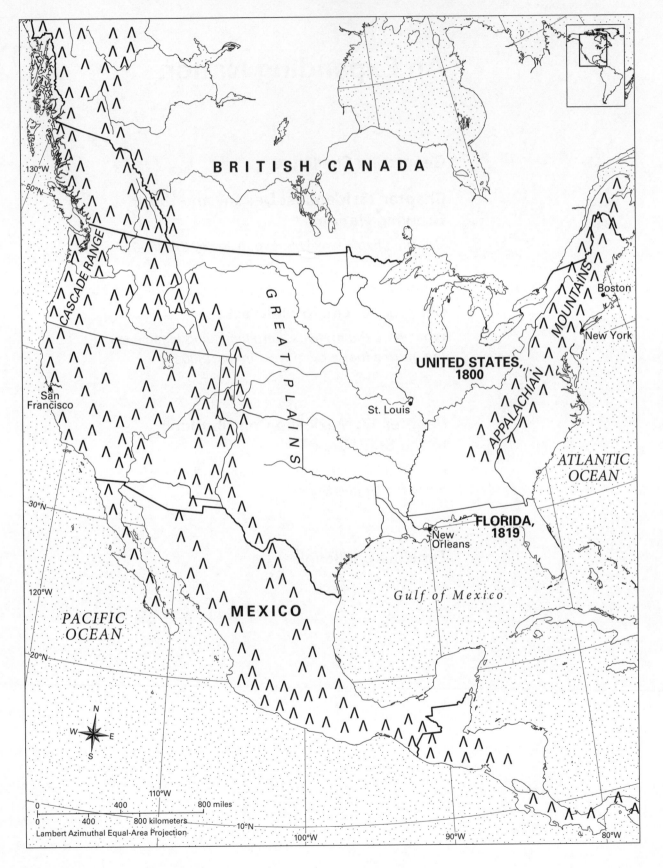

Geography Skills

Analyze the maps in "Setting the Stage" for Unit 5 in your book. Then answer the following questions and fill out the map as directed.

1. Label the Louisiana Territory on your map and highlight its borders. What year was it added to the United States? How did adding this region change the size of the nation?

2. Highlight the borders of Texas and the Mexican Cession and label these two regions. When was each region added to the United States?

    What other territory was acquired from Mexico? Label it on your map.

3. What three trails crossed the Louisiana Territory from Independence, Missouri? Draw and label each trail.

    Locate and label the cities at the ends of each trail. Also locate and label the city of Independence.

4. Label and lightly shade Oregon Country. When did it become part of the United States?

5. Draw and label the Old Spanish Trail. Locate and label its western end.

6. Which rivers and mountain ranges did settlers have to cross when following the Santa Fe Trail and the Old Spanish Trail to California? Label those rivers and mountains.

7. Locate and label Sacramento. Where did the trail that settlers took to reach this city leave the Oregon Trail? Locate and label that place on your map.

8. Locate and label South Pass. Which three trails crossed the Rocky Mountains at South Pass? Label and name those trails.

Critical Thinking

Answer the following questions in complete sentences.

9. Why do you think the Mormon, Oregon, and Santa Fe trails each followed rivers for such a long distance? What benefit would such a route have for travelers?

10. Why would travel by wagon through the mountains have been slower than travel across desert or plains?

11. How might the United States' purchase of the Louisiana Territory from France have helped encourage American settlers to later travel to Oregon and California?

Manifest Destiny and the Growing Nation

How justifiable was U.S. expansion in the 1800s?

PREVIEW

Your teacher will display a painting that is also reproduced at the beginning of Chapter 15 in your book. Begin to analyze the painting with your class, and then continue on your own or with a partner. *On a separate sheet of paper,* answer the questions below. Support your answers with evidence from the painting.

1. Which groups in the painting are moving from the east toward the west? What are they bringing with them?

2. What are some possible reasons these groups are moving west?

3. Which groups were already in the West? What is happening to them?

4. Who is the main figure in the center of the painting? What might she represent?

5. John Gast painted *American Progress* in 1872. Do you think he believed that U.S. expansion in the 1800s was justifiable? Why or why not?

READING NOTES

Key Content Terms

As you complete the Reading Notes, use these terms in your answers.

territory	Texas War for Independence	manifest destiny
diplomacy	annex	Mexican-American War

Section 15.2

1. Why were the city of New Orleans and the Mississippi River important to farmers in the early 1800s?

2. What was Napoleon's plan for Louisiana? Why were American farmers alarmed by it?

3. What deal was made on April 30, 1803? Give two reasons why Napoleon was willing to make this deal with the United States.

4. List two pros and two cons of the Louisiana Purchase.

Pros of the Louisiana Purchase	Cons of the Louisiana Purchase

Section 15.3

1. What did President Monroe order Andrew Jackson to do in 1818? What did Jackson do instead?

2. Explain the deal that the United States made with Spain in 1819 to end the conflict over Florida.

Section 15.4

1. List two complaints of American settlers in Texas in 1830. Then list two complaints of Tejanos in 1830.

American settlers:

Tejanos:

2. Complete the timeline with important events that led Texas to win its independence. Write a one- or two-sentence summary next to each date. Use all of the words in the Word Bank somewhere on the timeline. Also, create illustrations for two of the events.

Word Bank
the Alamo
General Santa Anna
immigration
Republic of Texas
"Remember the Alamo"
slavery
Stephen F. Austin
Tejanos

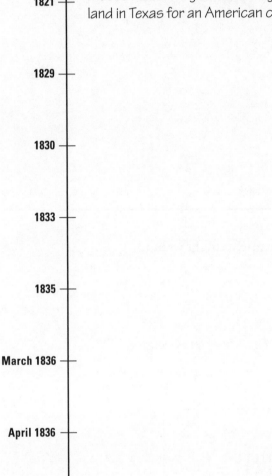

1821 — Moses Austin is granted a huge tract of land in Texas for an American colony.

1829 —

1830 —

1833 —

1835 —

March 1836 —

April 1836 —

1836–1845 —

3. What happened to Texas in 1845? Give one argument against and one argument in favor of this decision.

Section 15.5

1. What agreement did Great Britain and the United States make in the 1820s concerning Oregon?

2. Why Oregon was called a "pioneer's paradise"?

3. What did James Polk mean when he declared "Fifty-four forty or fight!" in the 1844 presidential campaign? Did he follow through with this campaign promise? Explain.

Section 15.6

1. Why did President Polk think the Mexican government might want to sell California and New Mexico?

2. Label the map with sentences to explain why the U.S. Congress declared war on Mexico in 1846.

Disputed Texas, 1846

3. Choose two of these Mexican-American War battle locations: New Mexico, California, Monterrey, Buena Vista, or Chapultepec. Then create two historical newspaper headlines for each of your two battle locations. Write the first headline for a U.S. newspaper whose editors agreed with manifest destiny. Write the second headline for a newspaper in Mexico.

Location 1: _____   **Location 2:** _____

| **Manifest Destiny Times** | | **Manifest Destiny Times** |

| **Tiempos de México** | | **Tiempos de México** |

4. List three details of the Treaty of Guadalupe Hidalgo. Then give two reasons some U.S. senators opposed this treaty.

5. Why did the United States buy the Gadsden Purchase in 1853?

PROCESSING

Below is a drawing of John Gast's painting *American Progress*. Annotate the drawing by adding a speech or thought bubble for four elements in the painting—people, animals, or objects. In each bubble, write a short paragraph to express how that person, animal, or object might respond to the Essential Question: *How justifiable was U.S. expansion in the 1800s?* Include as many of the Key Content Terms as possible in your paragraphs.

Preparing to Write: Taking Notes on Details

In her journal, Susan Magoffin recorded descriptions and details about her travels along the Santa Fe Trail. Because of this record, readers today can share her experiences. Take notes about the trip based on the descriptions in the reading.

When and where did the expedition begin?

Describe how the Magoffins outfitted themselves for the trip.

What happened at Pawnee Rock?

Describe Susan Magoffin's accident.

Explain why the Magoffins stopped at Bent's Fort.

Writing a Postcard

Suppose you were part of the Magoffin expedition. What if you could have sent a message home during your journey on the Santa Fe Trail? Use the space below to write a postcard to someone you have left behind in the United States. On your postcard, include

- descriptions and details about what you are seeing.
- a description of what you like and dislike about the trip.
- the date, a greeting, a closing, and your signature.

Use this rubric to evaluate your postcard. Make changes in your postcard if you need to.

Score	Description
3	The postcard has accurate descriptions and details. It is well constructed. There are no spelling or grammar errors.
2	The postcard has descriptions and details. It is well constructed. There are some spelling or grammar errors.
1	The postcard does not have descriptions and details. It is not well constructed. There are many spelling or grammar errors.

© Teachers' Curriculum Institute

Life in the West

*What were the motives, hardships, and legacies
of the groups that moved west in the 1800s?*

PREVIEW

Listen to the song "Sweet Betsy from Pike." Then, answer these questions
on another sheet of paper:

1. What is the mood of the song's melody?

2. Where is Sweet Betsy going?

3. What reasons or motives might she have for making this journey?

4. What hardships did she face along the way?

5. Why would Sweet Betsy—and pioneers like those in the painting at the
   beginning of Chapter 16 in your book—be willing to risk such hardships?

6. What kind of legacies do you think such pioneers might have left behind?

READING NOTES

Key Content Terms

As you complete the Reading Notes, use these terms in your answers.

Lewis and Clark expedition	rancho	Mormons
legacy	Oregon Trail	forty-niners

Section 16.2

1. List three motives, or reasons, for why
   the Lewis and Clark expedition explored
   the West.

2. Describe one hardship that the Lewis and
   Clark expedition faced.

3. What was the legacy of the Lewis and Clark expedition? Name at least two accomplishments.

4. What was the legacy of each of these explorers?

Zebulon Pike:

John C. Frémont:

Section 16.3

1. To which of these groups of people did the Mexican government award large grants of land in California? Circle your answers, and explain why these groups were given land.

   soldiers   settlers   California Indians

3. Name one hardship that Californios faced.

4. Draw and label a sketch showing what you think is the Californios' most important legacy.

2. List two activities commonly found at a rancho.

Section 16.4

1. Why did Manuel Lisa follow the route of Lewis and Clark west?

2. List three hardships that mountain men faced.

3. Would you have liked to have been a mountain man? Use details from the reading to explain why or why not.

4. Draw and label a sketch showing what you think is the mountain men's most important legacy.

Section 16.5

1. Why did missionaries like Marcus and Narcissa Whitman and Henry and Eliza Spalding move west?

2. Create a sketch showing the Whitmans' greatest success. Include Marcus Whitman in your sketch with a speech bubble explaining his motives for his work.

3. Describe one legacy of missionaries in the West.

Section 16.6

1. Many women moved west with their families. Why did single women pioneers move to the West?

2. List three hardships that women faced along the trail.

3. Explain how each of the following is an example of the great legacy of pioneer women.

    Biddy Mason:

    Annie Bidwell:

    Wyoming Territory:

Section 16.7

1. Why did Mormons move to the West?

2. Name two hardships that Mormons in the West faced.

3. Draw and label a sketch showing what you think is the Mormons' most important legacy.

Section 16.8

1. Why did many people move to California after 1848?

2. List three hardships that forty-niners faced.

3. Fill in the speech bubbles to describe the legacy of the forty-niners from the perspective of each group.

California Indian

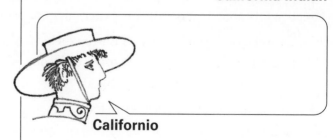

Californio

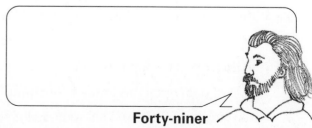

Forty-niner

1. What motivated many poor Chinese peasants to travel to California in the 1800s?

4. Draw and label a sketch showing what you think is the most important legacy of the Chinese.

2. What hardship faced by the Chinese caused them to leave the mines? How did some Chinese respond to this hardship?

PROCESSING

Create a folk song that details the experiences of people who moved west.

1. Choose a tune you know well for the melody. You might use "Sweet Betsy from Pike" or another folk song you know, such as "I've Been Working on the Railroad."

2. *On another piece of paper,* write four stanzas of four lines each. Each stanza should be about a different group of settlers.

3. Within the four lines of each stanza, include

   • at least one motive for this group to move to the West.

   • at least one hardship this group faced.

   • at least one legacy this group left behind.

4. Give your song a title, and tell what melody it is sung to.

Preparing to Write: Making Comparisons

Historians estimate that more than 300,000 people came to California during the gold rush. All of them had their own reasons for leaving home and for traveling to California. These are sometimes called *push factors* and *pull factors*. In other words, some factors pushed people to leave their homes, while other factors pulled them to California.

List the push and pull factors for four people you read about.

Traveler	Push Factors	Pull Factors
Luzena Wilson		
Thomas Kerr		
Vicente Pérez Rosales		
Alvin Coffey		

How were the push factors the same or different for these four people?

How were the pull factors the same or different for these four people?

Writing a Human-Interest Article

Suppose you were a newspaper journalist in 1850. Your assignment is to write a short human-interest article. A human-interest article focuses on the people involved in an event or situation. Your subject is people who were part of the gold rush.

For your article, "interview" one or more of the people described in the reading. Be sure to give background information on the gold rush as well as "quotations" from the people you interview.

Use this rubric to evaluate your article. Make changes in your article if you need to.

Score	Description
3	The article clearly focuses on human-interest stories about the gold rush. It includes background information and "quotations" that help the reader to understand the event. There are no spelling or grammar errors.
2	The article focuses on human-interest stories about the gold rush. It includes some background information and "quotations." There are few spelling or grammar errors.
1	The article does not focus on human-interest stories about the gold rush. It includes very little background information or "quotations." There are many spelling or grammar errors.

Mexicano Contributions to the Southwest

How have Mexicano contributions influenced life in the United States?

The following items were all important in the American Southwest in the 1800s. Circle the items that you think were Mexicano contributions.

adobe bricks

community property laws

irrigation ditches

ten-gallon hats

cattle-branding irons

corridos

patios

walnuts

chili (stew)

fandango (dance)

red-clay roof tiles

western saddles

citrus fruits

gold-mining pans

rodeos

Key Content Terms

As you complete the Reading Notes, use these terms in your answers.

Mexicanos   irrigation

Sections 17.2 to 17.10

If your class is doing the activity for this chapter, follow Steps 1 to 4 below.
(Note: If your class is not doing the activity, skip Steps 1 to 4. Read each section of the chapter, and complete all of the matrix on the following pages except for the first column.)

Step 1: With your partner, go to one of the placards. Carefully examine the image, and discuss Questions 1 and 2 on the placard.

Step 2: Find the appropriate section of your Reading Notes, and write your answers to Question 2 in the first column. Then check the correct answers on the back of the placard. Circle any of your answers that match.

Step 3: Discuss Question 3 with your partner. Then return to your seats. Read the corresponding section in your book, and complete the Reading Notes for that section.

Step 4: Repeat the Steps 1 to 3 with a new placard.

Mexicano Contributions to the Southwest

Topic	List details you think are Mexicano contributions.	Give three or more examples or details of Mexicano contributions from this section.
Mining Placard 17A Section 17.2		
Cattle Ranching Placard 17B Section 17.3		
The Cowboy Placard 17C Section 17.4		
Sheep Raising Placard 17D Section 17.5		
Irrigated Farming Placard 17E Section 17.6		

Describe how these contributions influenced settlers in the Southwest in the 1800s.	Describe how these contributions influenced life in the United States.	Create a symbol to represent this Mexicano contribution.

Mexicano Contributions to the Southwest

Topic	List details you think are Mexicano contributions.	Give three or more examples or details of Mexicano contributions from this section.
Food Placard 17F Section 17.7		
Architecture Placard 17G Section 17.8		
Laws Placard 17H Section 17.9		
Entertainment Placard 17I Section 17.10		

Describe how these contributions influenced settlers in the Southwest in the 1800s.	Describe how these contributions influenced life in the United States.	Create a symbol to represent this Mexicano contribution.

Mexicano Contributions to the Southwest **161**

PROCESSING

Create a collage of Mexicano contributions that are found in your community. You can create your collage below or on another sheet of paper. The items in your collage must come from at least three sections of the chapter. Your collage must include

- at least three or more colorful images (photographs you take, original drawings, or images from magazines or the Internet).

- a label for each image that includes the name of the contribution and the chapter section it relates to; for example, *Patio: Architecture.*

- one or two paragraphs that explain how these items have influenced or enhanced your life or the lives of Americans today.

Preparing to Write: Analyzing Purpose

An enormous project like *The Great Wall of Los Angeles* requires a lot of careful planning. This mural is divided into panels, each of which tells a story. The artists who created each panel had to decide the panel's purpose—the story they wanted to tell and why.

What was Judith Baca's purpose in designing the mural?

What story did she want to tell?

What purpose did the artists have in creating the Chavez Ravine panel?

What was the muralists' purpose in creating the "tattoo mural" in South Tucson, Arizona?

Writing a Design Proposal

Suppose you could help plan a mural like *The Great Wall of Los Angeles.* Think of a story you would like to tell about your community. You will have one panel in the mural for your story.

Write a design proposal for your mural panel. In your proposal, describe

- the purpose of the mural.
- the story you want to tell.
- how you will show the story in the mural.

Use this rubric to evaluate your design proposal. Make changes in your proposal if you need to.

Score	Description
3	The design proposal clearly describes the purpose and the story. It has sufficient details on how the story will be shown. There are no spelling or grammar errors.
2	The design proposal describes the purpose and the story. It has some details on how the story will be shown. There are few spelling or grammar errors.
1	The design proposal does not describe the purpose and the story. It does not have sufficient details on how the story will be shown. There are many spelling or grammar errors.

Timeline Skills

Analyze the Unit 5 timeline in your book. Also think about what you have learned in this unit. Then answer the following questions.

1. Which territories did the United States acquire during this time period? How did the nation acquire each of these territories?

2. What was the purpose of the Lewis and Clark expedition? How long did it last?

3. Name at least two reasons people moved to the American West in the 1800s.

4. Name at least three groups of people living in the West in the 1800s.

5. How long did the gold rush last? Name one of its impacts.

6. After the acquisition of the Louisiana Territory, how many years did it take for the United States to complete its spread across North America?

7. What was the Lone Star Republic? How many years did it last?

8. What motivated many Americans to support the Mexican-American War?

9. What happened in Wyoming Territory in 1869 for the first time in the nation's history?

Critical Thinking

Use the timeline and the chapters in the unit to answer the following questions.

10. Explain how manifest destiny influenced the westward expansion of the United States in the 1800s.

11. Choose at least three groups living in the West during the 1800s. Explain how you think each group felt about U.S. expansion into the West.

12. What do you believe is the most significant Mexicano contribution to life in the United States? Explain your opinion.

13. If you could add three more events to this timeline, which would they be? List each event, and explain why you think it is important enough to add to the timeline.

    a.

    b.

    c.

Americans in the Mid-1800s

Geography Challenge

Chapter 18: An Era of Reform
To what extent did the reform movements of the mid-1800s improve life for Americans?

Chapter 19: The Worlds of North and South
How was life in the North different from life in the South?

Chapter 20: African Americans in the Mid-1800s
How did African Americans face slavery and discrimination in the mid-1800s?

Timeline Challenge

The Slave Trade in the United States, 1808–1865

ATLANTIC
OCEAN

Gulf of Mexico

40°N
70°W

35°N

30°N

25°N

75°W

80°W 20°N

90°W

85°W

95°W

0   200   400 miles
0   200   400 kilometers
Albers Conic Equal-Area Projection

Geography Skills

Analyze the maps in "Setting the Stage" for Unit 6 in your book. Then answer the following questions and fill out the map as directed.

1. Outline the border of the slave states on your map. Which rivers were along the border between slave states and free states? Locate and label them.

2. Locate and label each of the slave states. Which of them had the largest slave population in 1860?

    Which slave state had the least number of slaves? How can you tell?

3. Find the major slave trade centers on the map in your book. What role did these cities have in the slave trade?

    Which cities outside the slave states were involved in the slave trade?

4. Which new slave states entered the Union between 1812 and 1845? Draw a star for each one.

5. Which three of the new slave states were most important to the growth and expansion of slavery? How can you tell?

6. From which three states were slaves sold in the slave market at Montgomery, Alabama, likely to have come? Write the state names here, and circle them on your map.

7. In which two states were slaves sold in Kentucky likely to end up? Write the state names here, and shade them on your map.

8. How were slaves transported to be sold in the slave markets at Pensacola and New Orleans? From which states were they transported? Underline those state names.

9. Which slave market was probably the main source from which slaveholders in Arkansas purchased slaves? Label this slave trade center.

Critical Thinking

Answer the following questions in complete sentences.

10. Why do you think most of the slaves sold to slaveholders in Texas arrived by sea?

11. Why do you think certain parts of the South had large numbers of slaves, while other parts did not?

12. From the routes shown on the slave trade map, why would it have been easy for slave traders to illegally bring slaves into the United States from islands in the Caribbean?

An Era of Reform

To what extent did the reform movements of the mid-1800s improve life for Americans?

PREVIEW

Read the lyrics to the song "Let Us All Speak Our Minds." Then answer these questions *on a separate sheet of paper:*

1. How would you describe the mood created by the lyrics?

2. Why do you think women would write and sing a song like this?

3. To what extent do you think the complaints mentioned in this song are still valid today?

READING NOTES

Key Content Terms

As you complete the Reading Notes, use these terms in your answers.

reform	transcendentalism	Seneca Falls Convention
Second Great Awakening	abolitionists	Declaration of Sentiments

Section 18.2

1. What was the optimistic message of the Second Great Awakening?

2. Explain how this quotation by Henry David Thoreau reflects the philosophy of transcendentalism: "If a man does not keep pace with his companions, perhaps it is because he hears a different drummer. Let him step to the music he hears."

3. How did transcendentalism contribute to the spirit of reform?

1. Complete the flowchart to show the conditions in prisons during the mid-1800s and the reforms that were passed.

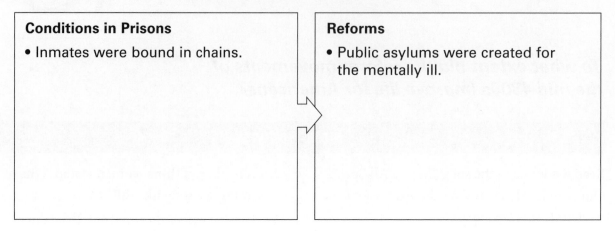

Conditions in Prisons
• Inmates were bound in chains.

Reforms
• Public asylums were created for the mentally ill.

2. Complete the sensory figure of Dorothea Dix to show her possible thoughts, feelings, and experiences.

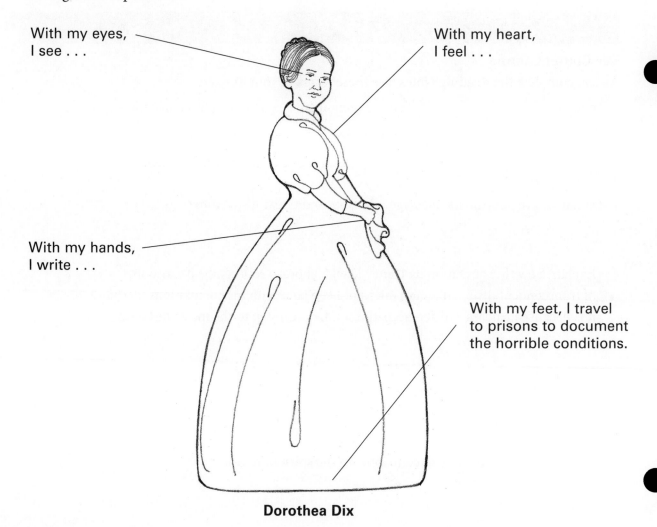

With my eyes, I see . . .

With my heart, I feel . . .

With my hands, I write . . .

With my feet, I travel to prisons to document the horrible conditions.

Dorothea Dix

1. Complete the flowchart to show the conditions of public education in the mid-1800s and the reforms that were passed.

Conditions of Public Education	Reforms
• Few areas had public schools.	• In Massachusetts, citizens voted to build better schools.

2. Complete the sensory figure of Horace Mann to show his possible thoughts, feelings, and experiences.

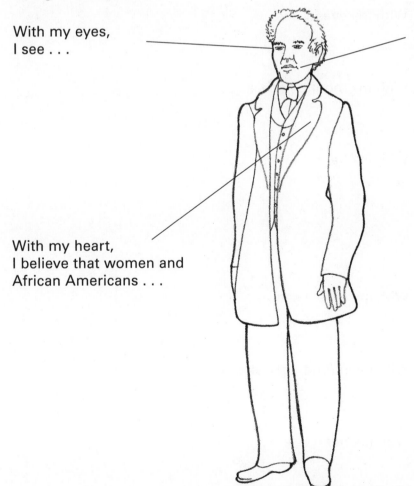

With my eyes,
I see . . .

With my mouth,
I speak out for . . .

With my heart,
I believe that women and
African Americans . . .

Horace Mann

Complete the sensory figures to show the possible thoughts, feelings, and experiences of each abolitionist.

With my ears, I hear . . .

With my heart, I feel . . .

With my hands, I write . . .

William Lloyd Garrison

With my eyes, I see . . .

With my mouth, I speak . . .

With my hands, I write . . .

Frederick Douglass

With my eyes, I see . . .

With my mouth, I speak out . . .

With my heart, I feel . . .

Sojourner Truth

1. Complete the flowchart to show the conditions of women in the mid-1800s
   and the reforms that were passed.

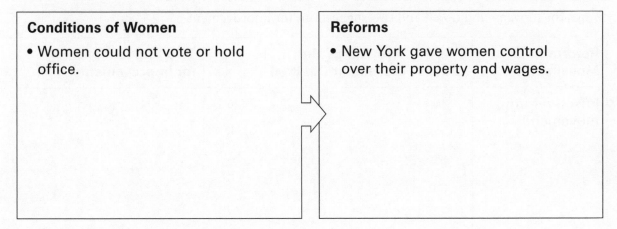

Conditions of Women	Reforms
• Women could not vote or hold office.	• New York gave women control over their property and wages.

2. Complete the sensory figure of Elizabeth Cady Stanton to show her possible
   thoughts, feelings, and experiences.

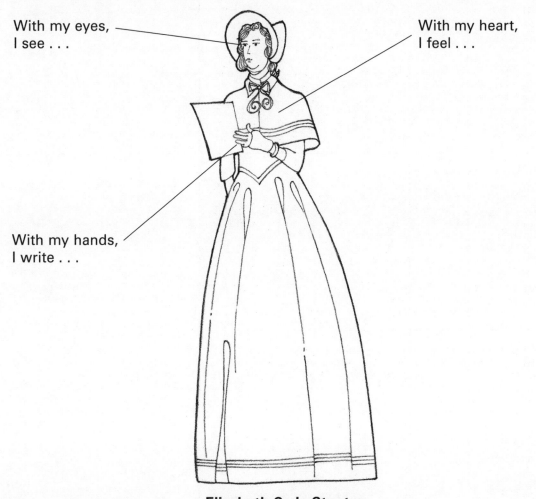

With my eyes,
I see . . .

With my heart,
I feel . . .

With my hands,
I write . . .

Elizabeth Cady Stanton

Evaluate the extent to which the reform movements of the mid-1800s improved life for Americans. For each reform movement, assign a grade. Then list two things the movement did well and two suggestions for improvement.

Reform Movement	Grade	Two Things the Movement Did Well	Two Suggestions for Improvement
Prison reform movement			
Education reform movement			
Abolitionist movement			
Women's rights movement			

Preparing to Write: Making Generalizations

Throughout history, people have dreamed of having a perfect life. More than 2,000 years ago, the Greek philosopher Plato imagined an ideal society. Almost 500 years ago, an English statesman and author, Sir Thomas More, coined the term *utopia* from the Greek words meaning "no place." In other words, utopia was a dream but not a reality.

Nevertheless, people have not stopped trying to create perfect societies. The Americans who created Brook Farm were no exception.

Many utopian communities were formed in the first half of the 1800s. What were their goals?

Why did George Ripley want to combine thinking and working at Brook Farm?

How did Brook Farm reflect the beliefs of transcendentalists?

Writing a Commercial

Suppose you could start a utopian community. What goals would you have for the community? How would you attract other people to join you?

Create a storyboard for a one-minute television commercial about your utopian community. Your storyboard should contain sketches and words to show what will happen in the commercial. The goals of your commercial are to inform people about your utopian community and to attract people to live there.

Use this rubric to evaluate your storyboard. Make changes in your storyboard if you need to.

Score	Description
3	The storyboard clearly communicates the goals of the commercial. The commercial will strongly motivate prospective members of the community. There are no spelling or grammar errors.
2	The storyboard communicates the goals of the commercial. The commercial might motivate prospective members of the community. There are few spelling or grammar errors.
1	The storyboard does not communicate the goals of the commercial. The commercial will not motivate prospective members of the community. There are many spelling or grammar errors.

The Worlds of North and South

How was life in the North different from life in the South?

Write the name of your community in the center of the spoke diagram. Then, for each spoke coming from "Geography," "Transportation," "Economy," and "Society," write a phrase or sentence that describes that aspect of your community. Also draw a simple sketch to illustrate each phrase or sentence. For example, if you live in Florida, you might write "hot climate" on one of the spokes from "Geography" and draw the sun.

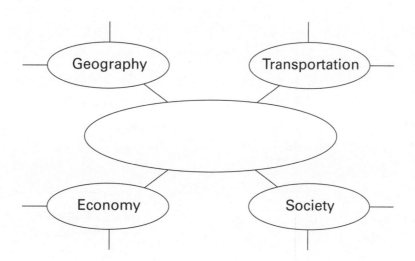

Key Content Terms

As you complete the Reading Notes, use these terms in your answers.

deforestation	plantation	Industrial Revolution	immigrant
agrarian	cotton gin	industrialist	

On the following pages, you will complete two spoke diagrams, one on the North and one on the South. After you read each section in your book, turn to the appropriate spoke diagram. Draw at least four spokes from the aspect of life you read about: "Geography," "Transportation," "Economy," or "Society." On each spoke, write a phrase or sentence describing one feature of that aspect of life. In the oval, make a sketch to illustrate that aspect of life.

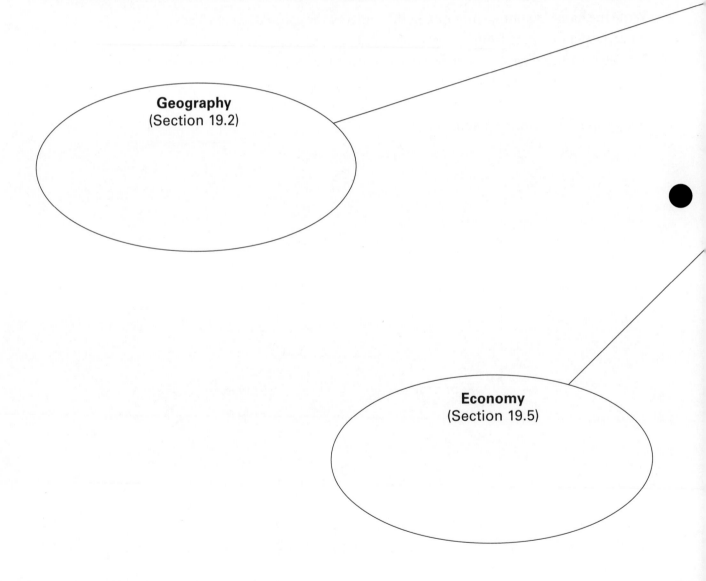

Geography
(Section 19.2)

Economy
(Section 19.5)

The World of the North

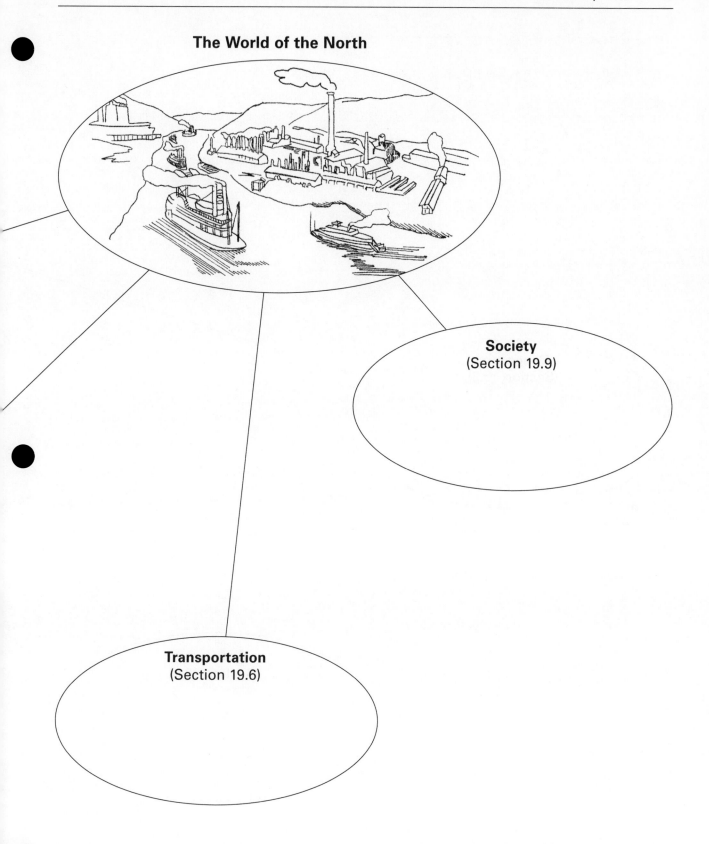

Society
(Section 19.9)

Transportation
(Section 19.6)

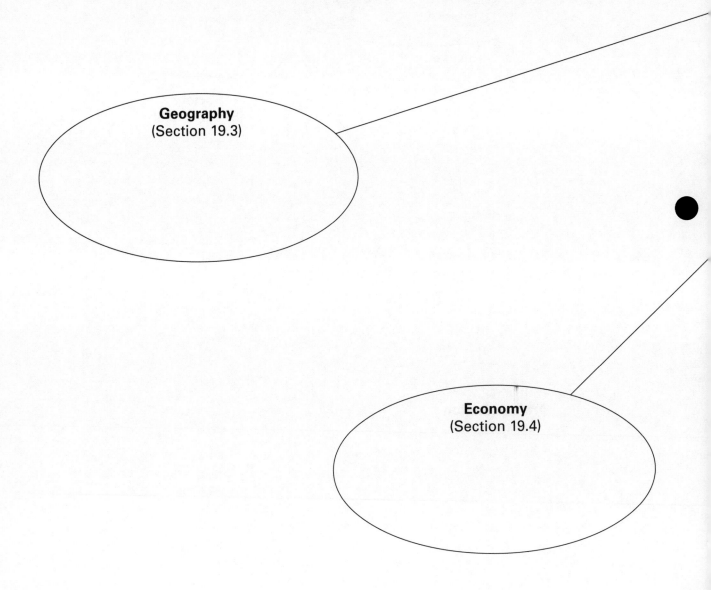

Geography
(Section 19.3)

Economy
(Section 19.4)

The World of the South

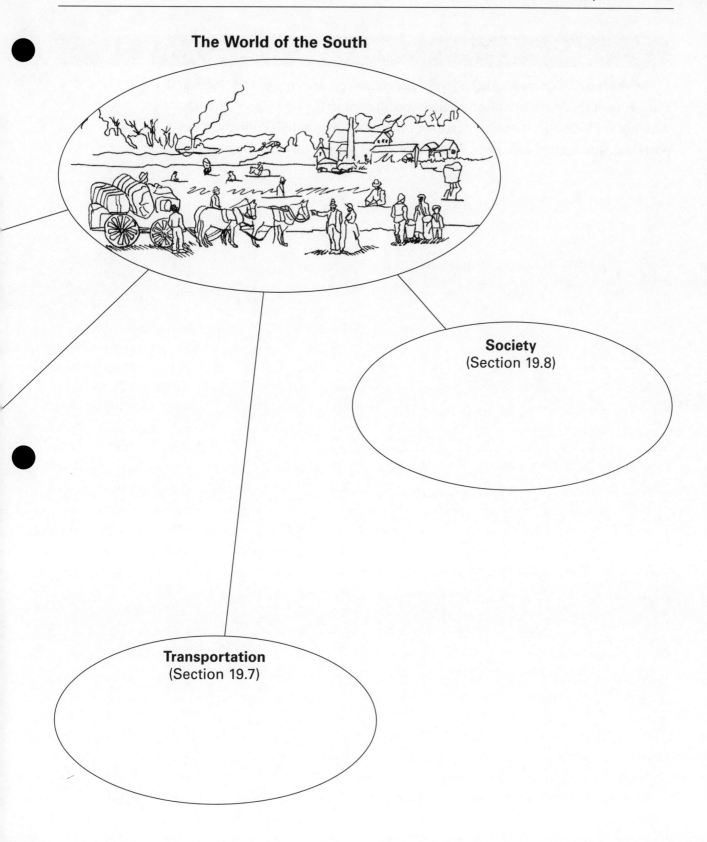

Society
(Section 19.8)

Transportation
(Section 19.7)

PROCESSING

In the space below or on another sheet of paper, make a drawing of the North and a drawing of the South to show how life was different in the two places. In each drawing, include at least one key feature of the area's geography, economy, transportation, and society. Label and describe each key feature on your drawings.

Preparing to Write: Recording Details

Primary source materials tell us a great deal about life during the Industrial Revolution. In Lowell, Massachusetts, for example, both mill workers and visitors described their experiences. They wrote letters, diaries, books, and newspaper articles. The details they recorded help us better understand that time and place.

Describe life in Lowell in the mid-1800s.

What would you have seen in the factories in Lowell?

Describe the people you would have seen in the factories.

Outside of the mills, what were workers' lives like?

Writing Diary Entries

Suppose you were a mill worker in Lowell in the mid-1800s. You are keeping a diary of your experiences. Write one entry to describe your feelings and experiences soon after you arrived in Lowell. Write a second entry to describe your feelings and experiences a year later. Include factual details in your entries.

Use this rubric to evaluate your diary entries. Make changes in your entries if you need to.

Score	Description
3	The diary entries clearly describe feelings and experiences. They include factual details. There are no spelling or grammar errors.
2	The diary entries describe feelings and experiences. They include details. There are few spelling or grammar errors.
1	The diary entries do not describe feelings and experiences. They do not include details. There are many spelling or grammar errors.

African Americans in the Mid-1800s

How did African Americans face slavery and discrimination in the mid-1800s?

PREVIEW

Listen to the song "Moses." Then, *on a separate sheet of paper,* answer these questions:

1. What three words describe the song's mood?

2. Who might King Pharaoh represent? What might the river Jordan represent?

3. What does the song tell us about how African Americans faced slavery?

READING NOTES

Key Content Terms

As you complete the Reading Notes, use these terms in your answers.

racism	segregation	Nat Turner's Rebellion
discrimination	Underground Railroad	oppression

Section 20.2

Compare the experiences and rights of slaves, free blacks in the South, and free blacks in the North. List at least three facts in each column.

Slaves	Free Blacks in the South	Free Blacks in the North

If the majority of white Southerners did not own slaves, why did the South remain
so loyal to slavery?

**If your class is doing the activity for this chapter, answer all four questions in each
section.** (Note: If your class is not doing the activity, answer only Questions 3 and 4.)

Section 20.4
Working Conditions of Slaves

1. Placard 20A matches Quotation _____
   because

2. Analyze the placard. Complete the
   sentences to describe how parts of a
   slave's body might feel.

   My fingers feel . . .

   My eyes feel . . .

   My legs feel . . .

3. Read Section 20.4. Record three details of
   the working conditions of slaves.

4. Sketch one symbol or illustration for a quilt
   block on this topic.

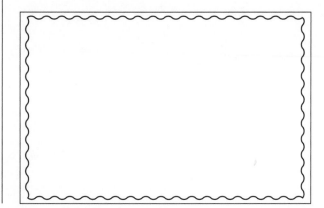

Section 20.5

Living Conditions of Slaves

1. Placard 20B matches Quotation _____ because

2. Analyze the placard. Describe how these slaves might feel about their situation.

3. Read Section 20.5. Give three details about the living conditions of slaves.

4. Sketch one symbol or illustration for a quilt block on this topic.

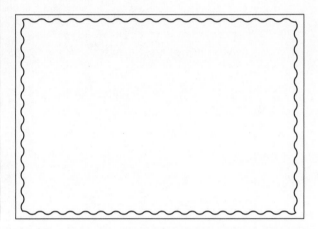

Section 20.6

Controlling Slaves

1. Placard 20C matches Quotation _____ because

2. Analyze the placard. How could this scene have happened?

3. Read Section 20.6. List three methods that slave owners used to control slaves.

4. Sketch one symbol or illustration for a quilt block on this topic.

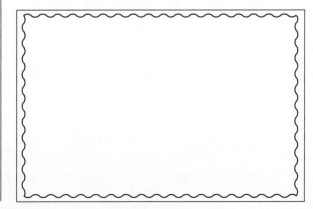

Section 20.7

Resistance to Slavery

1. Placard 20D matches Quotation _____ because

2. Analyze the placard. What is happening in the image?

3. Read Section 20.7. Give three examples of how slaves resisted slavery.

4. Sketch one symbol or illustration for a quilt block on this topic.

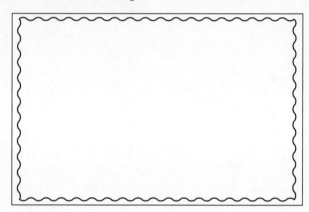

Section 20.8

Slave Families and Communities

1. Placard 20E matches Quotation _____ because

2. Analyze the placard. Describe how two of the people in this scene might feel about what is happening.

3. Read Section 20.8. Describe two ways slaves were able to maintain close families and communities.

4. Sketch one symbol or illustration for a quilt block on this topic.

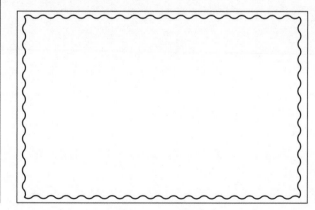

Section 20.9

Leisure Time Activities

1. Placard 20F matches Quotation _____ because

2. Analyze the placard. Describe what three of the people are doing.

3. Read Section 20.9. List three ways slaves spent their leisure time.

4. Sketch one symbol or illustration for a quilt block on this topic.

Section 20.10

Slave Churches

1. Placard 20G matches Quotation _____ because

2. Analyze the placard. Suppose you are a visitor to this scene, and describe what you see and hear.

3. Read Section 20.10. Explain why the idea of being invisible was important to slave churches.

4. Sketch one symbol or illustration for a quilt block on this topic.

Section 20.11

African American Culture

1. Placard 20H matches Quotation _____ because

2. Analyze the placard. Suppose you are a visitor to this scene, and describe what you hear.

3. Read Section 20.11. Record three aspects of African American life that had roots in African culture.

4. Sketch one symbol or illustration for a quilt block on this topic.

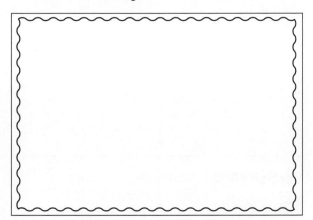

PROCESSING

On a separate sheet of paper, write a paragraph answering the Essential Question: *How did African Americans face slavery and discrimination in the mid-1800s?*

Support your answer with at least one piece of evidence from three of these topics:

- living conditions
- working conditions
- resistance efforts
- slave communities and families
- leisure time activities
- slave churches

Preparing to Write: Taking Notes

Thanks to the work of people like William Still, we have information about the life and work of Harriet Tubman.

When and why did Harriet Tubman escape from slavery?

List three facts that are known about Tubman's escape.

What led Tubman to become a conductor on the Underground Railroad?

List four facts about how Tubman operated as a conductor.

Why did people call Harriet Tubman "Moses"?

Writing a Short Biography

Suppose you have been asked to write a short biography of Harriet Tubman for a Web site about famous American women. Your biography should include factual information from the reading. Limit opinions to quotations from primary sources. Give details on Harriet Tubman's life and accomplishments.

Harriet Tubman (about 1820–1913)

Use this rubric to evaluate your biography. Make changes in your biography if you need to.

Score	Description
3	The biography gives many details about Tubman's life based on facts from the reading. It includes no personal opinions. There are no spelling or grammar errors.
2	The biography gives some details about Tubman's life based on facts from the reading. It includes no personal opinions. There are some spelling or grammar errors.
1	The biography does not give details about Tubman's life based on facts from the reading. It includes personal opinions. There are many spelling or grammar errors.

Timeline Skills

Analyze the Unit 6 timeline in your book. Also think about what you have learned in this unit. Then answer the following questions.

1. When was the cotton gin invented? Who invented it?

2. By 1841, where did the National Road extend?

3. Why was the building of the Erie Canal significant?

4. Who wrote *Walden*? What philosophy does the book reflect?

5. During what years did the nation experience a revival of religious feeling? What was this revival called?

6. What were the names of two antislavery newspapers established during this period? Who founded them?

7. What year was Nat Turner's Rebellion? What happened as a result of the rebellion?

8. What were two issues that Horace Mann campaigned for?

9. When did Harriet Tubman escape from slavery? About how many people did she guide to freedom on the Underground Railroad?

10. When and where was the Declaration of Sentiments signed?

Critical Thinking

Use the timeline and the chapters in the unit to answer the following questions.

11. How did the invention of the cotton gin transform the economy of the South?

12. Describe how the Second Great Awakening influenced the reform movements of the period.

13. What were three effects of the Industrial Revolution?

14. If you could add three more events to this timeline, which would they be? List each event, and explain why you think it is important enough to add to the timeline.

    a.

    b.

    c.

The Union Challenged

The United States, Mid-1850

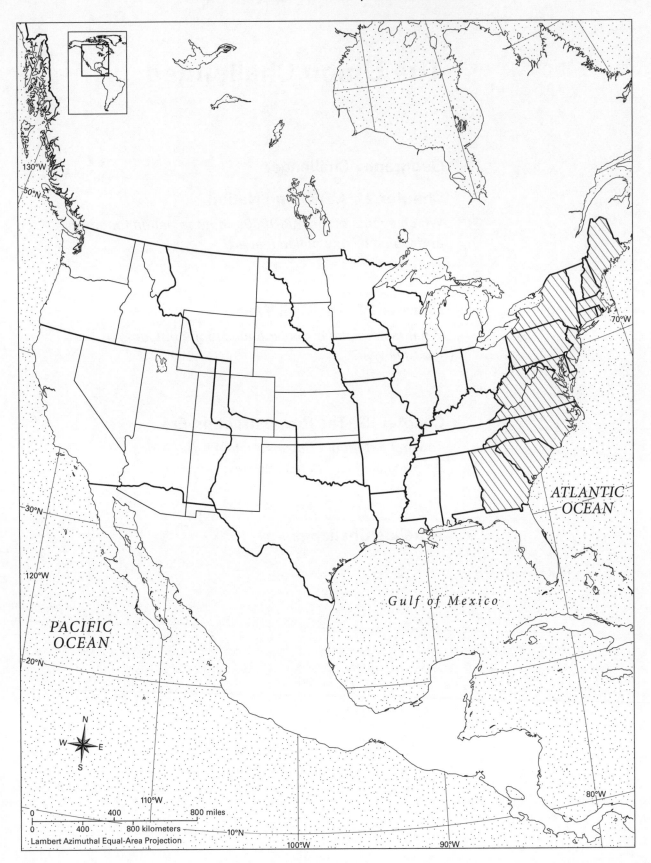

130°W
50°N
70°W
30°N
120°W
20°N

ATLANTIC
OCEAN

Gulf of Mexico

PACIFIC
OCEAN

N
W   E
S

110°W

0   400   800 miles
0   400   800 kilometers
Lambert Azimuthal Equal-Area Projection

10°N

100°W   90°W

80°W

Geography Skills

Analyze the maps in "Setting the Stage" for Unit 7 in your book. Then answer the following questions and fill out the map as directed.

1. Label the states that existed in mid-1850. How many of them allowed slavery? How many did not?

2. How many of the original 13 states were slave states, and how many were free states? Identify them by placing an *S* or an *F* under their names on your map.

3. Find the first 5 states that joined the Union following the original 13 states. Determine whether each was a slave state or a free state. Write an *S* or an *F* under the name of each.

   How many of these new states were slave states? How many were free states? What were the total numbers of slave states and free states as of 1812?

4. In what order did the next 6 states enter the Union? Place an *F* under the names of the free states and an *S* under the names of the slave states.

5. What pattern did Congress follow between 1816 and 1821 in admitting new states to the Union?

   How did this pattern affect the voting power of the North and South in the U.S. Senate?

6. Locate Arkansas and Michigan, and write their admission dates on your map. Did the admission of these states follow the pattern Congress set between 1816 and 1821? Why or why not?

7. Locate the last 4 states admitted to the Union before 1850, and write their admission dates on your map. How many of these states were slave states? How many were free states?

8. How did the admission of these 4 states affect the voting power of slave states and free states in the U.S. Senate?

9. Which slave state had the most votes in the House of Representatives in mid-1850? How many free states had more votes than this state?

10. Did the free-state North or the slave-state South control the House of Representatives in mid-1850?

Critical Thinking

Answer the following questions in complete sentences.

11. Why would California's application to become a state have caused a crisis over the issue of slavery?

12. Why might Southerners be more upset if California were admitted as a free state than Northerners might be if it were admitted as a slave state?

13. California entered the Union as a free state in 1850. In 1854, Congress began preparing Kansas to become a state. Why do you think the question of slavery in Kansas would be a highly controversial issue between the North and South?

14. Minnesota and Oregon were admitted to the Union as free states in 1858 and 1859. Then, in 1860, a man who opposed slavery was elected president. How do you think these events made Southerners feel about the future of slavery in the United States? Explain why.

A Dividing Nation

Which events of the mid-1800s kept the nation together and which events pulled it apart?

PREVIEW

In 1858, Abraham Lincoln warned, "A house divided against itself cannot stand."

Answer the following questions *on a separate piece of paper.*

1. What do you think the "house" in Lincoln's statement represents?

2. What might be dividing this house?

3. What do you think Lincoln meant by his statement?

READING NOTES

Key Content Terms

As you complete the Reading Notes, use these terms in your answers.

Union	Wilmot Proviso	Dred Scott decision
Missouri Compromise	Compromise of 1850	Lincoln-Douglas debates
fugitive	Kansas-Nebraska Act	

Section 21.2

1. Label the map to show how the Northwest Ordinance regulated slavery.

2. Fill in the speech bubbles to show two arguments in the debate over Missouri statehood.

Northerner

Southerner

3. Why was it important to Southerners to keep an equal number of senators from free states and slave states in Congress? Mention the defeat of the Tallmadge Amendment in your answer.

Section 21.3

1. What were the three decisions in the Missouri Compromise?

2. Rewrite John Quincy Adams's diary entry to explain how he felt about the Missouri Compromise.

> *I have favored this Missouri compromise, believing it to be all that could be effected [accomplished] under the present Constitution, and from extreme unwillingness to put the Union at hazard [risk]. If the Union must be dissolved, slavery is precisely the question on which it ought to break. For the present, however, the contest is laid asleep.*

March 3, 1820

Section 21.4

1. What was John Quincy Adams's 1839 antislavery proposal? What was the gag rule, and how did it affect his proposal?

Wilmot Proviso:

2. How did the fugitive slave issue and the Wilmot Proviso pull the nation apart?

Fugitive slave issue:

3. Why did Northerners in Congress accept California's application for statehood while Southerners rejected it?

Section 21.5

1. List four details of Henry Clay's plan to end the deadlock over the issue of California statehood.

2. Write a new sentence to correct the errors in this sentence: *Northerners and Southerners easily accepted the terms of the Compromise of 1850 and put their suspicions to rest once it had been passed.*

List two key details to describe each event in the chart. Also explain how each event pulled the nation apart.

Events After the Compromise of 1850	Two Key Details	How the Event Pulled the Nation Apart
Fugitive Slave Act passed		
Uncle Tom's Cabin published		
Kansas-Nebraska Act passed		
Raid on Lawrence, Kansas		
Beating of Senator Sumner		

1. Why did Dred Scott argue that he should be freed from slavery?

2. Choose and explain the two most important decisions that came out of the Supreme Court's Dred Scott decision.

3. Fill in the speech bubbles to show two different reactions to the Dred Scott decision.

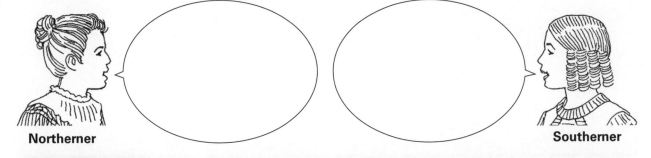

Northerner   **Southerner**

1. Besides helping Stephen Douglas win the 1858 Senate race in Illinois, what were two other results of the Lincoln-Douglas debates?

2. Why did John Brown attempt to seize the federal arsenal at Harpers Ferry, Virginia?

1. Create a newspaper headline to show how most Southerners reacted to the election of Lincoln in 1860.

> ## THE CHARLESTON MERCURY
> November 8, 1860

2. What happened in the South on each of these dates?

December 20, 1860:

February 1861:

3. What did Lincoln state about secession in his inaugural address on March 4, 1861? What was his appeal to the rebellious Southern states?

4. Create a newspaper headline to show how most Northerners reacted to the events at Fort Sumter in Charleston, South Carolina.

> ## The New York Tribune
> April 14, 1861

PROCESSING

A letter to the editor is a statement of your opinion on an issue about which you feel strongly. Choose the event that you believe pulled the nation furthest apart in the mid-1800s. *On a separate sheet of paper,* write a letter to the editor about that event. Your letter should be written from the time period of your event and should

- have an appropriate date.
- include your (fictitious) name and where you live.
- be one or two paragraphs long.
- briefly describe the event in one or two sentences.
- explain why you believe this event pulled the nation apart and eventually led to civil war.
- be free of grammatical and spelling errors.

Preparing to Write: Shaping Arguments

On many occasions, the Fugitive Slave Act of 1850 forced Americans to take sides on slavery. The 1854 capture of Anthony Burns and his return to slavery was one of those occasions. The people involved took very different positions about the fairness and legality of what happened.

Why did Anthony Burns go to Boston?

What do you think he expected his life to be like in Boston? Why?

What was the position of the U.S. government on Burns's right to live in Boston?

What was the position of Anthony Burns's master?

What was the position of Boston abolitionists?

Writing a Handbill

Create a handbill to protest the return of Anthony Burns to slavery. A handbill is a sheet of paper that you can hand out on the street. In your handbill, present at least two arguments for why Burns should not have been captured and sent back to Virginia. Explain each argument clearly.

Use this rubric to evaluate your handbill. Make changes in your handbill if you need to.

Score	Description
3	The handbill has at least two convincing arguments. It explains its points clearly. There are no spelling or grammar errors.
2	The handbill has a convincing argument. It explains its point. There are some spelling or grammar errors.
1	The handbill does not have convincing arguments. It does not explain its points. There are some spelling or grammar errors.

The Civil War

What factors and events influenced the outcome of the Civil War?

PREVIEW

Answer the following questions on *another sheet of paper*.

- How might real Civil War soldiers have felt marching off to war? Why?
- How do you think civilians watching the parade might have felt? Why?
- As the war progressed, how might key events and battles have affected or changed the way soldiers and civilians felt?

READING NOTES

Key Content Terms

As you complete the Reading Notes, use these terms in your answers.

Confederacy	Emancipation Proclamation	Gettysburg Address
civil war	habeas corpus	Appomattox Court House

Section 22.2

1. Complete the matrix. List at least five strengths or weaknesses for the North and five strengths or weaknesses for the South. Include any geographic strengths or weaknesses, and put a check next to them.

	Strengths	Weaknesses
North		
South		

2. Based on the information in your matrix, predict which side you think was more likely to win the Civil War. Explain your choice.

3. How did Abraham Lincoln and Jefferson Davis each use the ideals of the American Revolution and the Declaration of Independence to support their side's cause?

   Lincoln:

   Davis:

---

1. Explain each of the three steps of the Anaconda Plan.

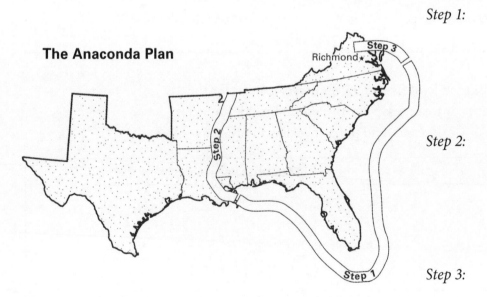

The Anaconda Plan

Richmond ★

Step 3

Step 2

Step 1

Step 1:

Step 2:

Step 3:

2. Who won the Battle of Bull Run? Describe the roles that Rose Greenhow and "Stonewall" Jackson played in the victory.

3. List five roles for women during the Civil War. Circle the role you would have wanted to fill if you were a woman at that time and tell why.

Section 22.4

1. Explain what the Union navy and army did to put each of the three steps of the Anaconda Plan into action from 1861 to 1862. Refer to your diagram from Section 22.3 to remind you of each step of the plan.

Step 1:

Step 2:

Step 3:

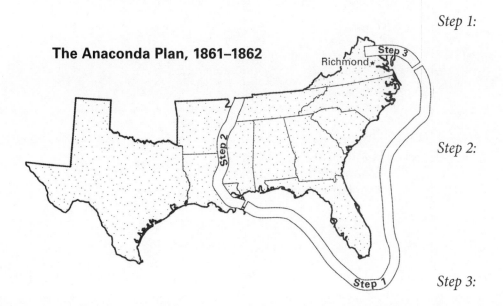

The Anaconda Plan, 1861–1862

Richmond ★

Step 3

Step 2

Step 1

2. Many soldiers who fought in the Battle of Antietam saw it as a defeat for both armies. Why? Support your answer with statistics.

3. Give three reasons why the death toll for soldiers in the Civil War was so high. Circle the reason that was the most deadly.

Section 22.5

1. Fill in the diagram with two reasons why Lincoln issued the Emancipation Proclamation and two important effects of his action.

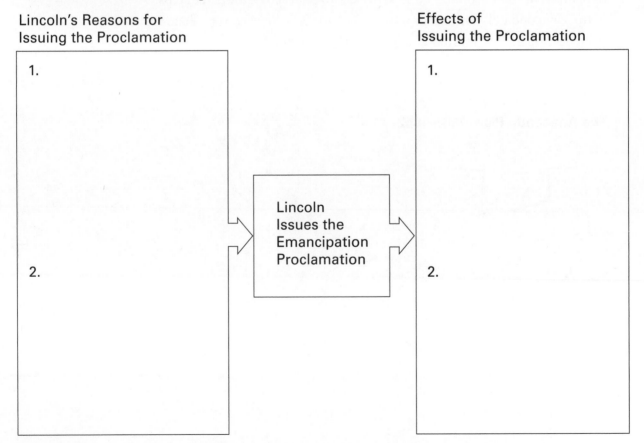

Lincoln's Reasons for
Issuing the Proclamation

1.

2.

Lincoln Issues the Emancipation Proclamation

Effects of
Issuing the Proclamation

1.

2.

2. Fill in the speech bubbles to show what General Lee might have said before and after the Battle of Gettysburg.

Before Gettysburg   **After Gettysburg**

3. Why did some Northerners oppose the war? How did President Lincoln respond when opposition turned violent?

4. Write a short excerpt from the Gettysburg Address that shows how Lincoln chose words to connect his speech to the Declaration of Independence. Then explain why you think he wanted to connect his address to the Declaration.

Section 22.6

1. Complete the spoke diagram. One entry has been started for you.

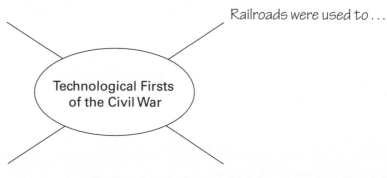

Railroads were used to . . .

Technological Firsts of the Civil War

2. Explain what the Union navy and army did to maintain or make progress on Steps 1 and 2 of the Anaconda Plan from 1862 to 1863.

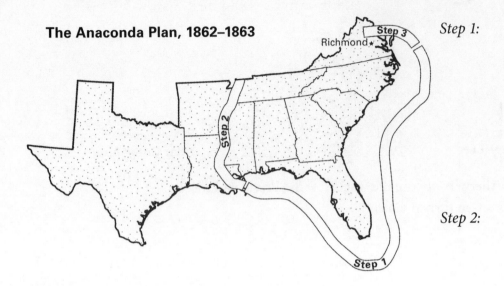

The Anaconda Plan, 1862–1863

Richmond ★

Step 3

Step 2

Step 1

Step 1:

Step 2:

3. Suppose you are a civilian in the South in 1864. Write a short letter to your father in the Confederate army telling him what life is like for civilians back home.

Fill in the Venn diagram to compare the experience of African American soldiers and white soldiers in the Union army. Give at least two important similarities and at least four key differences.

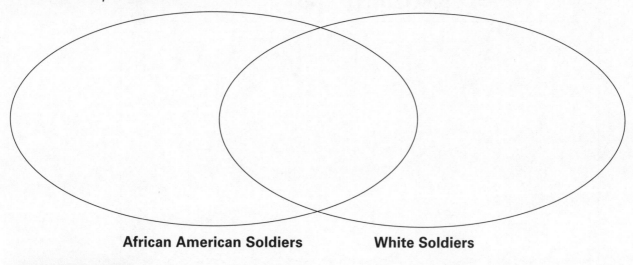

African American Soldiers   **White Soldiers**

1. Describe what General Grant meant by the term total war. Do you believe that total war is an appropriate war strategy? Why or why not?

2. Explain what the Union army did to complete Step 3 of the Anaconda Plan from 1864 to 1865.

The Anaconda Plan, 1864–1865   *Step 3:*

3. Write a newspaper headline and a short news article describing the event that occurred in Appomattox Court House on April 9, 1865. Be sure to include information on *what, who, when, where,* and *why*.

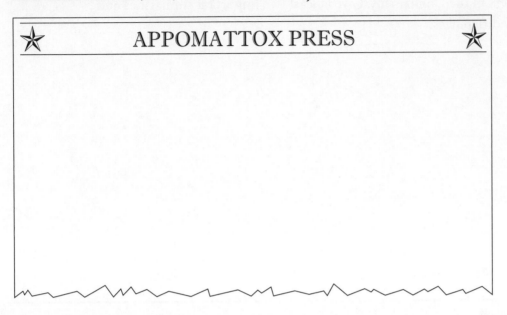

APPOMATTOX PRESS

4. There were many important results of the Civil War. Which do you think was the most important, and why?

PROCESSING

On a separate piece of paper, write a journal entry from the perspective of a soldier or a civilian during the Civil War. Your journal entry should include

- an historically accurate date and location (for example, July 4, 1863, near Gettysburg, Pennsylvania).

- one paragraph describing one of the key events or battles of the war so far.

- one paragraph describing your experiences as a soldier or as a civilian during that key event or battle and how it affected you. Use details from your Reading Notes or the classroom activity, and include relevant dialog and descriptions of specific actions.

- a sketch or photograph that relates to something you write about in your journal entry. Be sure to refer to this visual somewhere in your journal entry.

Preparing to Write: Identifying Emotions

In a civil war, the unity among groups in a nation falls apart. As Civil War congressman Elijah Babbit said, "Feuds . . . between members of the same families . . . are the most bitter of all feuds. Wars [between] the same people, are the most bloody."

As families and friends take sides in a civil war, they face powerful emotions, such as those in the Word Bank. Use some of the words listed to answer these questions.

How do you think Benjamin Hardin Helm felt about Abraham Lincoln's offer? Why?

How do you think Robert E. Lee would have felt if he had accepted Lincoln's offer? Why?

How do you think John J. Crittenden felt about his son George and the decision George made? Why?

Based on his letter, what emotions did James Campbell express to his brother after the Battle of Secessionville?

Word Bank
angry
disappointed
sad
happy
peaceful
loyal
bitter
honorable
conflicted
rebellious
fearful
proud

Writing a Personal Letter

Take the perspective of a young man or woman living in Kentucky in 1861. You would have supported one side in the Civil War. Using correct letter format, write to someone in your family who took the other side. Make a solid case for why you made the decision you did. Use words that express your emotions about your decision and theirs.

Use this rubric to evaluate your letter. Make changes in your letter if you need to.

Score	Description
3	The letter clearly explains your decision, using words that express emotions. It is written in correct letter format. There are no spelling or grammar errors.
2	The letter somewhat explains your decision but does not use words that express emotions. It is written in letter format. There are few spelling or grammar errors.
1	The letter does not explain your decision and does not use words that express emotions. It is not written in correct letter format. There are many spelling or grammar errors.

The Reconstruction Era

To what extent did Reconstruction bring African Americans closer to full citizenship?

PREVIEW

Suppose that you are an emancipated slave in the South at the end of the Civil War. What changes do you hope for your new life? *On a separate sheet of paper,* write about three ways you imagine your life will change now that you have your freedom.

READING NOTES

Key Content Terms

As you complete the Reading Notes, use these terms in your answers.

Reconstruction	black codes	Fifteenth Amendment
Thirteenth Amendment	civil rights	Jim Crow laws
Freedmen's Bureau	Fourteenth Amendment	

Section 23.2

1. What were President Johnson's two major aims for Reconstruction? Circle the aim that was achieved by the Thirteenth Amendment.

2. Who established the Freedmen's Bureau, and what was its purpose? List three activities of the bureau that helped it carry out its purpose.

3. Complete the chart to show how new Southern state governments limited African Americans in the South.

Black Codes Enacted During Presidential Reconstruction

Purpose	Example

Section 23.3

1. How did the Radical Republicans' aim for Reconstruction differ from President Johnson's? What two new laws passed by Congress helped them achieve this aim?

2. Place an adjective on the line below to describe the relationship between Congress and President Johnson during presidential Reconstruction. In each oval, give an example of this relationship.

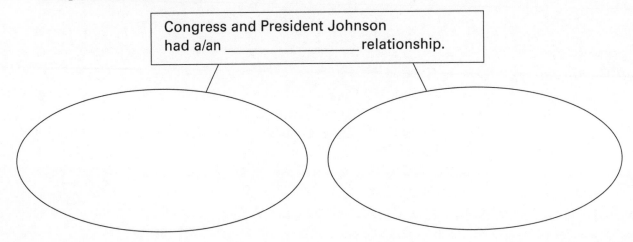

Congress and President Johnson had a/an _____ relationship.

3. Why did the House of Representatives impeach President Johnson? What was the outcome of the impeachment trial?

4. Why did many sharecroppers end up in poverty and debt?

Section 23.4

1. Who was banned by Congress from voting, and who were the three groups of new voters in the South? Write each answer on top of the appropriate symbol.

2. What important lesson did Republicans learn in the 1868 presidential election of Ulysses S. Grant?

1. On the spoke diagram, write a one-sentence summary of each change during Southern Reconstruction.

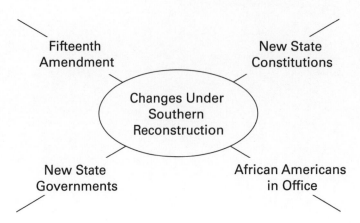

Fifteenth Amendment

New State Constitutions

Changes Under Southern Reconstruction

New State Governments

African Americans in Office

Section 23.5

1. Complete the flowchart to show the development and effects of violence against African Americans in the South.

↓

Southern Democrats tried to use legal means to keep blacks from voting or taking office.

↓

↓

↓

2. What was the dispute in the presidential election of 1876? How was it resolved?

3. How did the 1876 election affect African Americans in the South?

Section 23.6

1. How did Southern Democrats reverse gains made during Reconstruction in each of these areas?

   Education:

   Voting rights:

   Segregation:

2. Make a sketch to illustrate the results of *Plessy v. Ferguson*. Include a caption that explains the Supreme Court's decision in the case and the consequences of that decision.

1. List two factors that pushed African Americans out of the South after Reconstruction and two factors that pulled them toward the North.

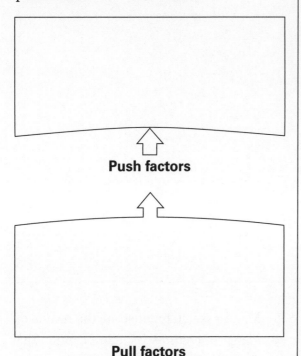

Push factors

Pull factors

2. Write one sentence to describe the experience of African Americans in each region at the end of the 1800s.

The North:

The West:

The South:

PROCESSING

On a separate sheet of paper, create an illustration of a road that shows the important events of Reconstruction and their impact on African Americans' journey toward full citizenship. Your road should

- show the progress and setbacks that African Americans experienced in their struggle for full citizenship during Reconstruction. For example, hills, twists, and turns away from full citizenship might show setbacks, while straight paths and bridges might show progress.

- include symbols, pictures, and labels for at least two events from each phase of Reconstruction. Stop signs, potholes, and roadblocks might show events that prevented progress toward full citizenship. High-speed-limit signs or freeway signs might show events that helped African Americans to achieve their goals.

- include at least six Key Content Terms.

- have a caption summarizing to what extent Reconstruction brought African Americans closer to full citizenship.

- be colorful and free of spelling errors.

Preparing to Write: Identifying Values

In 1965, President Lyndon Johnson told the U.S. Congress that the struggle of African Americans in Selma was a struggle shared by the nation. "Their cause must be our cause too," he said. President Johnson expressed his values by saying that it was important for *all* Americans to be able to exercise their civil rights.

What values were the Little Rock Nine expressing by integrating Central High School?

What values did Charles Houston act on when he trained black lawyers?

What values did the Selma marchers express through their actions?

Writing a Personal Statement

The right to vote is one of the most important values in a democratic nation. Americans have fought and died to defend that right. American citizens are able to exercise their right to vote when they are 18 years old.

Write a statement expressing your personal beliefs about the value of the right to vote. Offer two reasons why voting is important in a democracy. Tell whether you intend to vote when you are 18, and explain the reasons for your answer.

Use this rubric to evaluate your personal statement. Make changes in your statement if you need to.

Score	Description
3	The statement gives two reasons for the importance of voting. It clearly explains a personal opinion. There are no spelling or grammar errors.
2	The statement gives a reason for the importance of voting. It explains a personal opinion. There are some spelling or grammar errors.
1	The statement does not give reasons for the importance of voting. It does not explain a personal opinion. There are many spelling or grammar errors.

Timeline Skills

Analyze the Unit 7 timeline in your book. Also think about what you have learned in this unit. Then answer the following questions.

1. What was the Missouri Compromise? How long was it in effect?

2. Why did some Southerners threaten to secede over California's application for statehood?

3. How did the Kansas-Nebraska Act affect the Great Plains?

4. How did the Dred Scott decision affect slaves?

5. When was Abraham Lincoln elected president? What was an important result of his election?

6. What event started the Civil War? How long did the war last?

7. How many years of the Civil War passed before President Lincoln freed the slaves? In particular, which slaves were freed?

8. What two events took place in Gettysburg, Pennsylvania, in the same year? Why was each of these events significant?

9. When and where did the Civil War end?

10. Describe three changes to the Constitution after the Civil War that improved the lives of African Americans.

Critical Thinking

Use the timeline and the chapters in the unit to answer the following questions.

11. How did Congress try to keep the Union together? In your opinion, why did this ultimately fail?

12. Most people in 1861 expected the North to easily defeat the South and quickly win the war. Why did the war last for four years, proving this assumption false?

13. Do you believe Reconstruction was a success? Explain your opinion.

14. If you could add three more events to this timeline, which would they be? List each event, and explain why you think it is important enough to add to the timeline.

    a.

    b.

    c.

Migration and Industry

Major Railroads in the United States, 1870

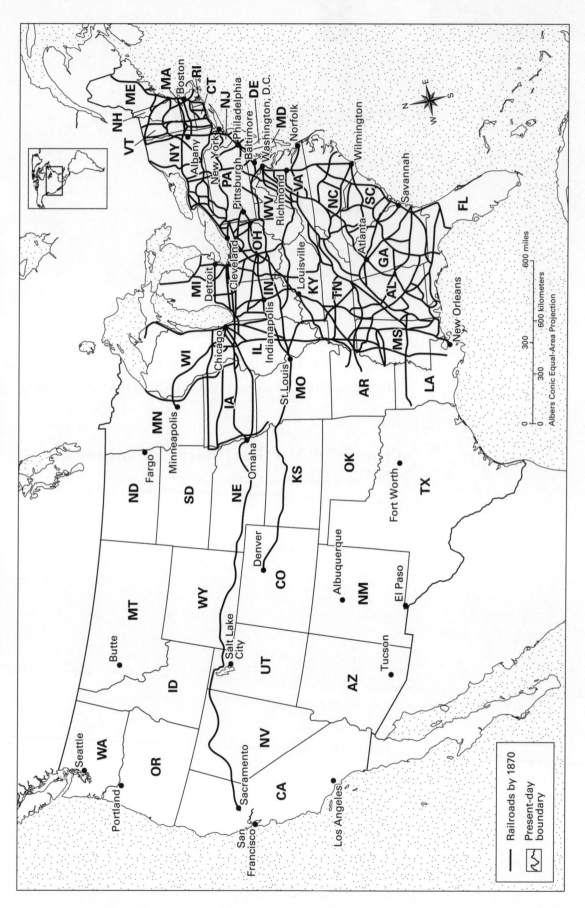

Geography Skills

Analyze the maps in "Setting the Stage" for Unit 8 in your book. Then answer the following questions and fill out the map as directed.

1. The eastern end of the only train track across the United States in 1870 was a city in Nebraska (NE). Which city was that? Which city was at that track's western end? Find both cities on your map and underline their names.

2. According to the population density maps in your book, how did settlement around Omaha, Nebraska, change between 1870 and 1890?

3. The builders of the first transcontinental railroad began at each end of the route and worked toward the middle. The two tracks met at the Great Salt Lake. Circle where they met on your map. In which present-day state is their connecting point located?

4. The railroad map in your book shows that by 1890, two more transcontinental railroads connected Seattle and Lake Superior. Draw those two railroad lines. Through which two towns did the southern route between Seattle and Lake Superior pass?

   Through which present-day states did both lines pass?

5. By 1890, a railroad line connected Denver and Albuquerque to the first transcontinental railroad. Draw that railroad line. How did the population near Albuquerque change between 1870 and 1890?

   How did the population near Denver change?

6. Draw the line that by 1890 had extended the railroad from Iowa into what is now South Dakota. How did the population of eastern South Dakota change by 1890?

   How was settlement affected at the western end of this railroad line?

7. Draw the two railroad lines that connected New Orleans and St. Louis with Fort Worth, Texas, in 1890. How did the population around Fort Worth change between 1870 and 1890?

8. Draw the two railroad lines running northwest from Minneapolis that were completed between 1870 and 1890. How did the population of western Minnesota and eastern North Dakota change during that period?

Critical Thinking

Answer the following questions in complete sentences.

9. Why might the population growth around Omaha by 1890 have been related to completion of the transcontinental railroad?

10. Based on what you have learned from this activity and on the maps in your book, do you think there was a connection between railroads and western population growth? Why or why not?

11. Do you think the West's population grew because of the railroad or because the railroad followed population growth to places where people were already living? Explain your answer.

Tensions in the West

How did settlers change the West and affect American Indians?

PREVIEW

On a separate piece of paper, write about a time when someone made a promise to you and then broke it. Describe what the promise was, why the person broke the promise, and how you felt when it was broken.

READING NOTES

Key Content Terms

As you complete the Reading Notes, use these terms in your answers.

reservation   transcontinental railroad

homesteader   subsidy

Section 24.2

Complete the sensory figure of Chief Joseph to show his possible thoughts, feelings, and experiences.

With my eyes,

With my mouth,

With my heart,

With my arms, I guide my fast Appaloosa horse, who helps a great buffalo hunter.

Section 24.3

How did the Homestead Act and the Pacific Railways Act bring settlers to the West?

For each reading section, draw a symbol to represent the settlers discussed in that section. Then fill in that row of the matrix.

	Who the Settlers Were	Reasons for Moving West
Section 24.4: Railroad Builders (symbol)		
Section 24.5: Miners (symbol)		
Section 24.6: Ranchers and Cowboys (symbol)		
Section 24.7: Homesteaders (symbol)		

Challenges Faced by Settlers	How Settlers Changed the West	Effect on American Indians

1. For each year on the timeline, briefly describe the federal policy or event that resulted in American Indians being moved onto reservations. Also draw a symbol to represent that policy or event.

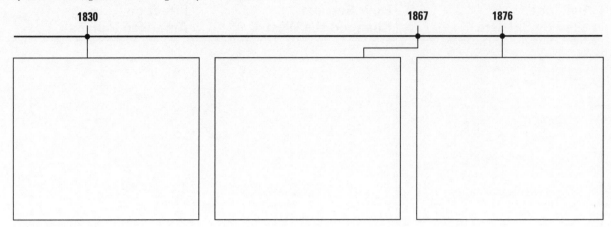

2. What do you think Sitting Bull was referring to when he said, "For when an Indian is shut in one place, his body becomes weak"?

PROCESSING

On a separate sheet of paper, write two acrostic poems about the clash of cultures that resulted from the settlement of the West. One poem should be from the perspective of white settlers. The other should be from the perspective of American Indians. Begin the lines in each poem with the letters in the word *settlement.* Two examples are given below.

Settlers' View of Settlement of the West	American Indians' View of Settlement of the West
Swiftly we came by railroad and horse.	Settlers invaded our lands from the East.
E	E
T	T
T	T
L	L
E	E
M	M
E	E
N	N
T	T

Preparing to Write: Taking Notes on Details

More than 50,000 African Americans left their homes and migrated west in the late 1870s. Individuals and families had both unique and shared experiences.

What conditions motivated African Americans to leave the South in the 1870s?

What drew the migrants to Kansas and other states?

What were two difficulties the migrants faced in making their exodus?

Describe the houses that many of the migrants lived in once they settled.

How did the new lives of most migrants compare to their lives in the South?

Writing a Diary Entry

Suppose you were an African American living in the South in 1879 who decided to migrate to Kansas. Choose one of the following times in your life: making the decision to leave, on the way west, arriving in Kansas, or five years after you settle. Write a diary entry describing that time. Include feelings and experiences in your entry, based on factual details.

Use this rubric to evaluate your diary entry. Make changes in your entry if you need to.

Score	Description
3	The diary entry clearly describes both feelings and experiences. It includes factual details. There are no spelling or grammar errors.
2	The diary entry describes some feelings and experiences. It includes some details. There are few spelling or grammar errors.
1	The diary entry does not describe both feelings and experiences. It does not include factual details. There are many spelling or grammar errors.

The Rise of Industry

Did the benefits of industrialization outweigh the costs?

PREVIEW

Think about the inventions or innovations that have occurred in your lifetime. *On a separate sheet of paper,* make a simple sketch of the invention or innovation that you think has most affected your life. Then, in a sentence or two, explain how it has affected you.

READING NOTES

Key Content Terms

As you complete the Reading Notes, use these terms in your answers.

entrepreneur	mass production	trust	urbanization
laissez-faire	corporation	monopoly	labor union

Section 25.2

1. How did federal, state, and local governments encourage business expansion?

2. Fill in the T-chart to compare the benefits of industrialization with its costs.

Benefits of Industrialization	Costs of Industrialization

In the first column of the matrix, draw a symbol to represent each invention.
Then complete the second and third columns.

Invention	Inventor	Impact of the Invention
Bessemer process (symbol)		
Electrical power station (symbol)		
Telephone (symbol)		
Mass production (symbol)	Several people contributed to this invention, which was made popular by Henry Ford.	
Airplane (symbol)		

1. How did John D. Rockefeller and Andrew Carnegie increase the size of their businesses?

2. What did the *Chicago Tribune* mean when it warned that "liberty and monopoly cannot live together"?

Complete the flowchart to show the effects of urbanization on the nation.

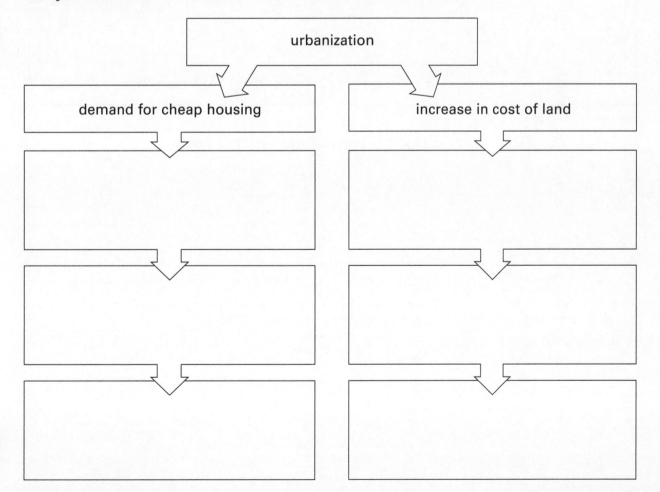

Complete the journal entry about a typical workday at the Triangle Factory.

July 17th, 1908

It was so hot in the factory today that . . .

1. What tactics did labor unions employ to improve working conditions?

2. How successful were labor unions in improving working conditions? Give at least one example.

© Teachers' Curriculum Institute

If your class is doing the activity for this chapter, complete the matrix below.

(Note: If your class is not doing the activity, skip this matrix.)

Complete the matrix to compare the classroom experience of making shirtwaist blouses to history.

Classroom Experience	Historical Connection
Students created individual shirts.	Craftspeople worked from their homes to produce textiles as part of the cottage industry.
	Mass-production techniques, like assembly lines, enabled workers to produce more goods per day at less cost.
Students were more productive with pencils and full sheets of paper than with crayons and half-sheets of paper.	
	Many businesses merged during the Industrial Revolution to be more productive.
	Many companies moved to big cities, where factory space was limited.
Immigrants were willing to replace workers for fewer points.	
	Working conditions in factories were usually poor.
Students' bodies and hands hurt from drawing the same part over and over.	
	Assembly workers became alienated from their supervisors.
Some students complained and threatened to strike.	

PROCESSING

On a separate sheet of paper, write a dialogue between a factory owner and a worker that highlights the costs and benefits of industrialization in the early 1900s. Your dialogue must

- begin with these opening lines:

  Worker: The workers in this factory aren't happy. They demand changes!

  Owner: You are lucky to be working in this modern factory!

  Worker: I've got a list of complaints and I demand to know what you will do about them. To begin with, . . .

- contain at least four concerns of workers at the turn of the century.
- contain a response by the factory owner to each concern.
- use these terms: *assembly line, working conditions, labor unions, strike, profit.*
- use language that reflects the passionate feelings of workers and owners.
- be free of spelling and grammatical errors.

Preparing to Write: Identifying Effects

Thomas Edison is known as a man who revolutionized the world. His inventions changed people's everyday lives in profound ways.

Edison did not actually invent most of the conveniences that W. G. Lathrop described in her letter. What do these devices have in common, for which she thanks the inventor?

What made the phonograph seem magical when it was first invented?

What were some practical uses of the phonograph that Edison suggested?

How do you think the first electric lights would have changed people's lives?

In what way does a movie do "for the Eye what the phonograph does for the Ear"?

Writing an Explanatory Paragraph

W. G. Lathrop gave Thomas Edison credit for all of the electrical appliances and machines in her home. How would your life be different if Edison had not invented a successful lightbulb or figured out how to distribute electricity throughout neighborhoods? Write a paragraph explaining how your life would be different without Edison's electrical inventions.

Use this rubric to evaluate your paragraph. Make changes in your paragraph if you need to.

Score	Description
3	The paragraph gives multiple differences between life with and without electricity. There are no spelling or grammar errors.
2	The paragraph gives some differences between life with and without electricity. There are some spelling or grammar errors.
1	The paragraph does not give differences between life with and without electricity. There are many spelling or grammar errors.

The Great Wave of Immigration

What was life like for immigrants in the early 1900s?

PREVIEW

On a separate sheet of paper, draw a simple sketch of someone crossing a border. Add a thought bubble to your drawing, explaining why this immigrant is leaving his or her homeland. Add a second thought bubble explaining what he or she expects in the new country.

READING NOTES

Key Content Terms

As you complete the Reading Notes, use these terms in your answers.

refugee	pogrom	nativism
assimilation	passport	quota

Section 26.2

1. Complete the sensory figure of an immigrant to show her possible thoughts, feelings, and experiences.

With my eyes,

With my mouth,

With my hands,

With my feet, I crossed over mountains and swam across rivers to arrive as a refugee in this country.

2. What contributions did immigrants make to the United States?

Section 26.3

1. List at least three important details about Italian immigrants' journey to the United States. Include information about why they left Italy, their voyage, and their experiences at Ellis Island.

2. List at least three important details about Italian immigrants' life in the United States. Include information about their living conditions, the work they did, and how people already living in the country treated them.

3. In the bag, draw at least two artifacts from an Italian immigrant's journey to the United States. Briefly explain what each artifact is.

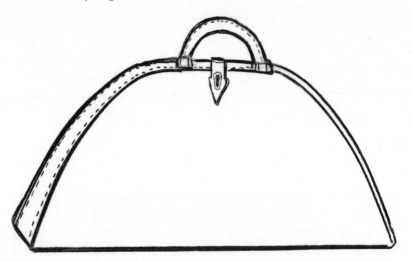

© Teachers' Curriculum Institute

1. List at least three important details about Jewish immigrants' journey to the United States. Include information about why they left eastern Europe, their voyage, and their experiences at Ellis Island.

2. List at least three important details about Jewish immigrants' life in the United States. Include information about their living conditions, the work they did, and how people already living in the country treated them.

3. In the trunk, draw at least two artifacts from a Jewish immigrant's journey to the United States. Briefly explain what each artifact is.

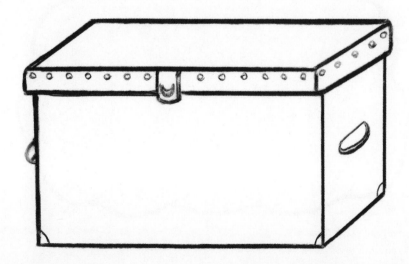

Section 26.5

1. List at least three important details about Chinese immigrants' journey to the United States. Include information about why they left China, their voyage, and their experiences at Angel Island.

2. List at least three important details about Chinese immigrants' life in the United States. Include information about their living conditions, the work they did, and how people already living in the country treated them.

3. In the bundle, draw at least two artifacts from a Chinese immigrant's journey to the United States. Briefly explain what each artifact is.

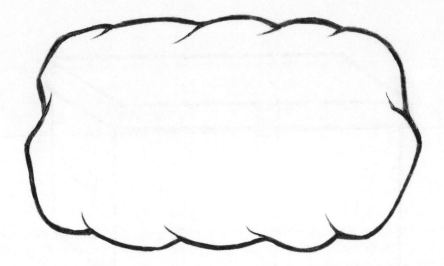

Section 26.6

1. List at least three important details about Mexican immigrants' journey to the United States. Include information about why they left Mexico, their voyage, and their experiences crossing the border.

2. List at least three important details about Mexican immigrants' life in the United States. Include information about their living conditions, the work they did, and how people already living in the country treated them.

3. In the backpack, draw at least two artifacts from a Mexican immigrant's journey to the United States. Briefly explain what each artifact is.

1. Why did nativism begin to rise in the 1880s?

2. How did Congress respond to the surge in nativism?

PROCESSING

Suppose you are an immigrant to the United States at the turn of the last century. *On a separate sheet of paper,* write a letter to a family member in your native country describing your trip to the United States and your experiences so far in this country. Be sure to include

- a brief description of why you left your native country.

- a description of your trip to the United States.

- a description of where you live and what life is like in the United States.

Preparing to Write: Asking Good Questions

The five young immigrants you read about were interviewed by writers. The writers asked them questions and recorded their answers. Later, the writers took the information they had collected and wrote books that included the immigrants' stories.

Read each statement below. Then write a question the interviewer might have asked to get that answer.

Manyang

Answer: "Gunmen attacked my village in the civil war that was fought in Sudan for many years."

Question:

Inayet

Answer: "Some of them were mean to me. They told me to go back to my own country."

Question:

Pang Houa

Answer: "I speak and act like any other American now."

Question:

Yulia

Answer: "My parents have different values than I do now."

Question:

Tito

Answer: "Immigrants have helped this country grow and prosper."

Question:

Writing Interview Questions

If you were to write a book about young immigrants in the United States today, what would you like to know? Make a list of ten questions you would ask the immigrants you interview. Your questions should include information about

- leaving home and arriving in the United States.
- differences between their old and new lives.
- challenges they have faced.
- likes and dislikes about their new lives.

Use this rubric to evaluate your interview questions. Make changes in your questions if you need to.

Score	Description
3	The questions cover all the listed topics. They are well constructed to obtain relevant information. There are no spelling or grammar errors.
2	The questions cover some of the listed topics. They will obtain some relevant information. There are few spelling or grammar errors.
1	The questions do not cover the listed topics. They will not obtain relevant information. There are many spelling or grammar errors.

Timeline Skills

Analyze the Unit 8 timeline in your book. Also think about what you have learned in this unit. Then answer the following questions.

1. When was the Transcontinental Railroad completed? Why was this railroad significant?

2. What act gave settlers 160 acres of free land in the West?

3. What happened at the Battle of the Little Big Horn?

4. When and why were Plains Indians relocated onto reservations?

5. Where did most immigrants go after arriving in the United States? Why?

6. What were two labor strikes that occurred during this period? Did strikers achieve their aims?

7. When did the United States establish an immigrant quota system? What was the purpose of this system?

8. When was the lightbulb invented? About how many years later was the first electrical power and distribution system built?

9. When and where did the Wright brothers fly the first airplane?

Critical Thinking
Use the timeline and the chapters in the unit to answer the following questions.

10. How did inventions and improved technology in this period help businesses become more efficient and improve the lives of many Americans? Give at least two examples.

11. What challenges did immigrants face in the United States? How did they overcome these challenges?

12. How did western settlement affect American Indians? Give at least two examples.

13. If you could add three more events to this timeline, which would they be? List each event, and explain why you think it is important enough to add to the timeline.

    a.

    b.

    c.

A Modern Nation Emerges

U.S. Territorial Expansion, 1867–1903

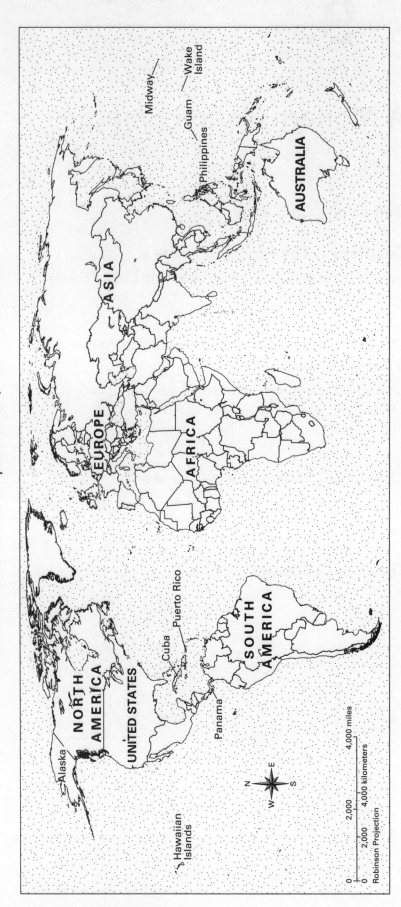

NORTH AMERICA

UNITED STATES

Alaska

Hawaiian Islands

Cuba

Puerto Rico

Panama

SOUTH AMERICA

ASIA

EUROPE

AFRICA

Midway

Wake Island

Guam

Philippines

AUSTRALIA

N
E
S
W

4,000 miles

4,000 kilometers

2,000

2,000

0

0

Robinson Projection

Geography Skills

Analyze the maps in "Setting the Stage" for Unit 9 in your book. Then answer the following questions and fill out the map as directed.

1. Which territory did the United States obtain from Russia? Shade it in on your map. In what year was this territory added to the United States?

2. Which U.S. possession was the greatest distance from the United States? Circle its name on your map.

3. Which two places were not U.S. possessions but were under U.S. control? Circle their names.

4. Which possessions did the United States gain as a result of its war with Spain? Circle their names.

5. Draw a box around Midway and study its location. Why do you think this island group was given this name?

6. What is the location of Wake Island relative to Midway?

7. What is the relative location of Guam from the Philippines?

8. Most of the U.S. areas of expansion suggest that Americans in the late 1800s were interested in trade with places on which continent? Circle the name of this continent on your map.

Critical Thinking

Answer the following questions in complete sentences.

9. How would acquiring the territories shown on the map have helped the United States achieve its goal of more trade with the continent you identified in Question 8?

10. Locate Panama on your map. How might having a canal through this region have helped the United States achieve its trade goals? (**Hint:** Think about where in the United States most manufacturing was located at that time.)

11. How might having control over Cuba and Puerto Rico help the United States protect the Panama Canal?

The Progressive Era

Did the progressives improve life in the United States?

List at least three problems that might have existed in American society at the time this song, *Future America,* was written.

Future America

My country 'tis of thee,
Land of lost liberty,
Of thee we sing.
Land which the millionaires,
Who govern our affairs,
Own for themselves and heirs,
Hail to thy king.

Land once of noble braves,
But now of wretched slaves,
Alas! too late!
We saw sweet Freedom die,
From letting bribers, high,
Our unpriced suffrage buy,
And mourn thy fate.

Land where the wealthy few,
Can make the many do,
Their royal will.
And tax for selfish greed,
The toilers till they bleed,
And those, not yet weak-kneed,
Crush down and kill.

READING NOTES

Key Content Terms

As you complete the Reading Notes, use these terms in your answers.

Progressive movement	platform	conservation
National Grange	social Darwinism	suffrage
Populist Party	regulation	

Section 27.2

1. The National Grange had a significant impact following the Civil War. Number the sentences from 1 to 7 to show the order in which the events occurred.

_____ By the mid-1870s, the National Grange had grown into a political force.

_____ In a series of cases, the Supreme Court sided with the Granges, strengthening the idea that government has a responsibility to protect the common good.

_____ As conditions improved, membership in the Granges dropped.

_____ After the Civil War, many farmers struggled and felt victimized by banks and big business.

_____ Big businesses protested this interference and sometimes sued.

_____ Self-help clubs for farmers, called Granges, sprang up all over the Midwest.

_____ Pressure from Grangers led some states to pass laws limiting railroad shipping rates and prices for grain storage.

2. How did the Populist Party hope to break the power of big business to dictate government policy?

3. Explain the meaning of this sentence: *William McKinley's victory was a triumph for people opposed to radical change.*

Write an adjective for this person under his or her name.	How would this individual answer this question: *Is there something wrong in America?* Explain.	Did this individual improve life in the United States? Give at least one example supporting your opinion.	What question would you like to ask this individual?
Section 27.3 Andrew Carnegie, Industrialist			
Section 27.3 John D. Rockefeller, Industrialist			
Section 27.4 Theodore Roosevelt, Progressive			

Write an adjective for this person under his or her name.	How would this individual answer this question: *Is there something wrong in America?* Explain.	Did this individual improve life in the United States? Give at least one example supporting your opinion.	What question would you like to ask this individual?
Section 27.5 Robert La Follette, Progressive _____			
Section 27.6 Mother Jones, Progressive _____			
Section 27.7 John Muir, Progressive _____			

Write an adjective for this person under his or her name.	How would this individual answer this question: *Is there something wrong in America?* Explain.	Did this individual improve life in the United States? Give at least one example supporting your opinion.	What question would you like to ask this individual?
Section 27.8 W. E. B. Du Bois, Progressive			
Section 27.9 Upton Sinclair, Progressive			
Section 27.10 Alice Paul, Progressive			

Review the lyrics to the song *Future America* from the Preview. Select one of the characters from the panel discussion, and write another verse to the song from his or her perspective.

- If you choose a progressive, the verse should mention what he or she believed was wrong in American society (such as trusts, political corruption, or unequal treatment for African Americans) and actions he or she took to solve the problem and improve life in the United States.

- If you choose an industrialist, the verse should describe what he thinks is right in American society and what he did to improve life in the United States.

Here is an example of a verse written from John Muir's perspective.

> Polluted environment,
> Nat'ral resources nearly spent,
> Redwood trees cut down.
> Instead create Yosemite,
> Reserves where birds fly free,
> To protect animals, earth, and trees,
> We are duty-bound.

Preparing to Write: Building Arguments

As the number of working children rose, so did the demands for reform. In 1913, the National Child Labor Committee (NCLC) published a declaration of children's rights. It included this resolution:

> *Resolved I—That childhood is endowed with certain inherent and inalienable rights, among which are freedom from toil for daily bread; the right to play and to dream; the right to the normal sleep of the night season; the right to an education, that we may have equality of opportunity for developing all that there is in us of mind and heart.*

You probably take these rights for granted. A hundred years ago, working children did not.

If you worked in a coal mine around 1900, how long might your day have been?

What were some of the hardships you would have faced?

If you were a child laborer in 1900, why did your family want you to work?

Why do you think reformers wanted children to go to school?

Writing a Persuasive Speech

Compose a short speech (one or two paragraphs) in favor of laws against child labor. Write from the perspective of a reformer in 1913, and use evidence from the previous page. Use one of the rights in the NCLC declaration as an argument for why young children should not work. Explain how that right is denied to working children and why you believe it is important for a child to have.

Use this rubric to evaluate your speech. Make changes in your speech if you need to.

Score	Description
3	The speech makes a strong argument in favor of child labor laws, based on one right from the NCLC declaration. It clearly explains the right and its importance. There are no spelling or grammar errors.
2	The speech makes an argument in favor of child labor laws, based on one right from the NCLC declaration. It lists the right and its importance, but does not clearly explain them. There are few spelling or grammar errors.
1	The speech does not make an argument in favor of child labor laws. There are many spelling or grammar errors.

The United States Becomes a World Power

Should U.S. actions in world affairs around the turn of the 20th century be praised or condemned?

Political cartoons express a cartoonist's opinion on a current issue through the use of images and words. Cartoonists may use several artistic devices in their cartoons, including important people, symbols, exaggerated details, and captions. Examine the political cartoon your teacher is projecting, and answer these questions.

1. What people or symbols do you see in this cartoon? Who or what might they represent?

2. What details, if any, are exaggerated in this cartoon? Why might they be exaggerated?

3. What does the caption say? How might it relate to the cartoon?

READING NOTES

Key Content Terms

As you complete the Reading Notes, use these terms in your answers.

imperialism   yellow journalism   nationalism   militarism

1. Fill in the T-chart with at least two arguments for and two arguments against U.S. expansionism around the turn of the 20th century.

Arguments for U.S. Expansionism	Arguments Against U.S. Expansionism

2. Complete the chart to show the sequence of events in the U.S. annexation of Hawaii.

1835 — Boston merchant establishes a sugar plantation in Hawaii.

1887 —

1891 —

1898 —

1. Complete the spoke diagram.

Causes of the Spanish-American War

2. List two results of the Spanish-American War as outlined in the peace treaty with Spain.

Section 28.4

1. Why were Filipino fighters willing to ally themselves with Admiral Dewey and the United States? Why did they eventually feel betrayed by the United States?

2. Fill in one speech bubble with praise for U.S. actions in the Philippines and the other with condemnation.

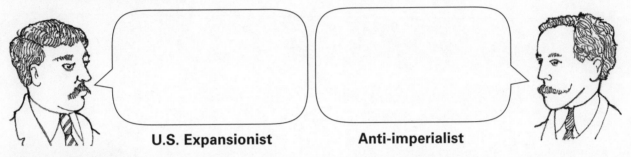

U.S. Expansionist   **Anti-imperialist**

Section 28.5

1. Complete the flowchart to show how the United States gained control of the Panama Canal.

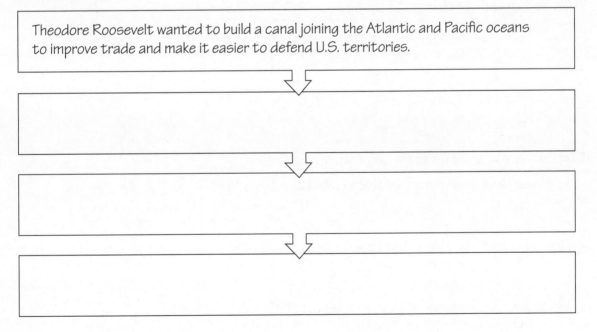

Theodore Roosevelt wanted to build a canal joining the Atlantic and Pacific oceans to improve trade and make it easier to defend U.S. territories.

2. In your opinion, what was the most difficult aspect of building the Panama Canal?

1. How did European countries try to stay safe in the years before 1914?

2. Create an illustration to explain the outbreak of World War I. Include and label the following: Austria-Hungary, Serbia, Russia, Germany, France, Great Britain, Central Powers, Allied Powers.

Section 28.7

1. Draw and label three changes in warfare during World War I.

2. Explain the war at sea by answering these questions.
   - Why was the German navy unable to use its surface ships?

   - How did Germany plan to blockade British ships?

   - What was the *Lusitania* and what happened to it?

   - What promise did Germany make after the *Lusitania* incident, and how did the promise affect U.S. manufacturers?

1. Why did President Wilson ask Congress to declare war on Germany on April 6, 1917?

2. Make a list of five ways the United States helped the Allies win World War I. Circle the factor you believe was the most significant, and explain why.

1. What were the key characteristics of each of these proposals for a postwar agreement? List at least two details in each of the three spaces of the Venn diagram.

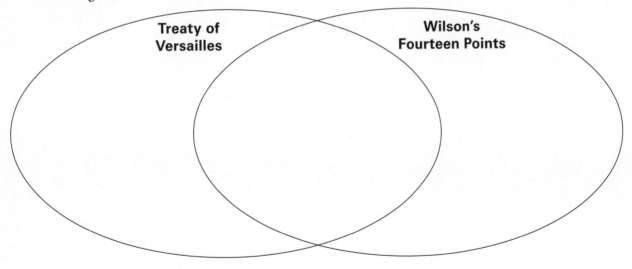

2. Why did the U.S. Senate reject the Treaty of Versailles and participation in the League of Nations?

PROCESSING

Create a political cartoon that shows your praise or condemnation of one of these topics: U.S. expansionism around the turn of the century or the U.S. role in World War I. Your cartoon should clearly convey your point of view on U.S. actions for that topic. It should also contain at least three of the following elements:

- symbols (images that represent something else)
- important people
- exaggerated details
- a caption
- other devices such as labels, speech balloons, or thought bubbles

Preparing to Write: Identifying Bias

William Randolph Hearst was a businessman, and his goal was to sell newspapers. At the height of his success, more than a million readers every day felt they *had* to read what he published. To create this excitement, Hearst urged his reporters to exaggerate or even to make up facts. He also encouraged *bias,* or presenting information and opinions that promote a particular point of view.

How did Hearst use the story of Evangelina Cisneros to promote his views about Cuba and the Spanish?

How was the *New York Journal* biased in its descriptions of the Cuban rebels and the Spanish rulers?

In what ways did the *New York Journal* manipulate the truth about the explosion of the U.S.S. *Maine*?

Writing a Newspaper Article

In the rules of journalism, a newspaper article should report facts as accurately as possible. A reporter should not write with bias or express opinion. If facts are in dispute, a reporter might interview people on different sides but should not take sides. Yellow journalism did not follow these rules. The articles that appeared in the *Journal* and the *World* on the explosion of the U.S.S. *Maine* are examples of yellow journalism.

Write the first paragraph of an unbiased article on the explosion of the *Maine*. Do your best to address the questions *who, what, where,* and *when,* but remember to only use facts that you know or believe to be true. Also, write a headline for your article.

Use this rubric to evaluate your paragraph. Make changes in your paragraph if you need to.

Score	Description
3	The headline and paragraph present factual information that addresses *who, what, where,* and *when.* There are no biased statements. There are no spelling or grammar errors.
2	The headline and paragraph present some factual information. There are no biased statements. There are few spelling or grammar errors.
1	The headline and paragraph do not present factual information. There are biased statements. There are many spelling or grammar errors.

Linking Past to Present

What changes since 1914 have shaped how we live today?

PREVIEW

Think about events in your life that have shaped how you think and behave today. Perhaps your grandfather took you to baseball games when you were young, and now you love to play baseball. Or maybe you often visited the zoo with your parents, and now you hope to become a veterinarian.

Choose one event that happened to you before you entered middle school, and explain how it is connected to some event or situation in your life today.

READING NOTES

Key Content Terms

As you complete the Reading Notes, use these terms in your answers.

feminist	globalization	knowledge worker
mass media	service sector	communism

Choose three events from Section 29.2 that you believe have most shaped how we live today. Label those events on the timeline below, along with the date and a one-sentence summary of each event. Also draw a simple illustration to represent each event. Finally, draw a line from each event to the correct place on the timeline.

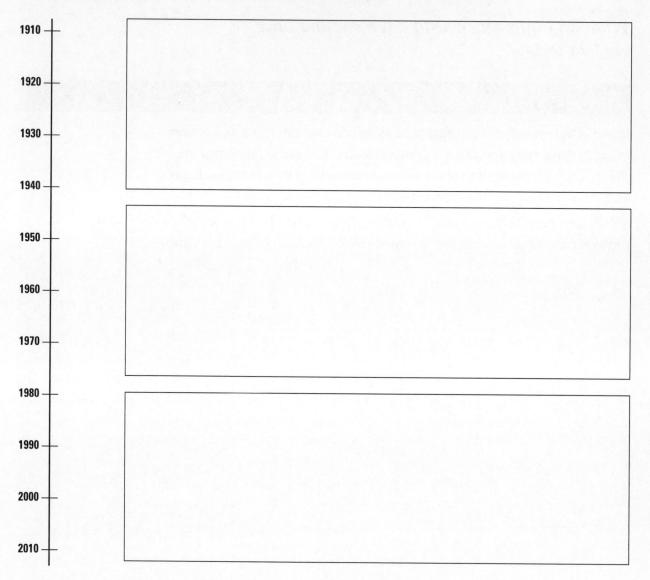

1910

1920

1930

1940

1950

1960

1970

1980

1990

2000

2010

Explain how one of the events on your timeline has shaped how we live today.

Choose three events from Section 29.3 that you believe have most shaped how we live today. Label them on the timeline below. Include the date, a one-sentence summary, and an illustration for each event. Draw a line from the event to the correct place on the timeline.

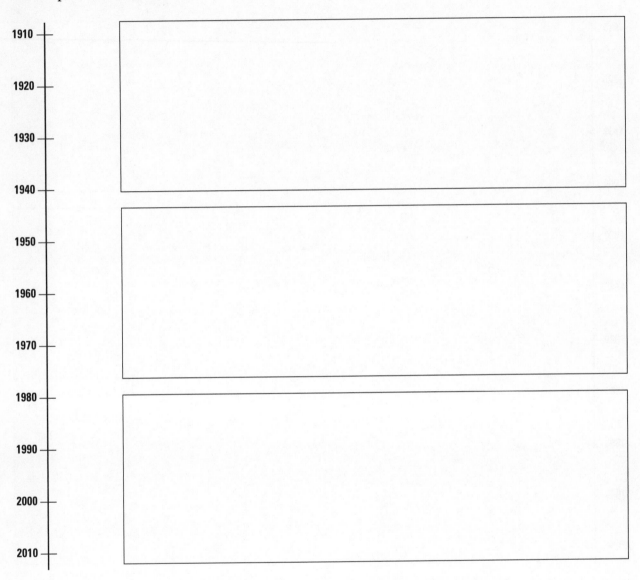

| 1910 |
| 1920 |
| 1930 |
| 1940 |
| 1950 |
| 1960 |
| 1970 |
| 1980 |
| 1990 |
| 2000 |
| 2010 |

Explain how one of the events on your timeline has shaped how we live today.

Choose three events from Section 29.4 that you believe have most shaped how we live today. Label them on the timeline below. Include the date, a one-sentence summary, and an illustration for each event. Draw a line from the event to the correct place on the timeline.

1910	
1920	
1930	
1940	
1950	
1960	
1970	
1980	
1990	
2000	
2010	

Explain how one of the events on your timeline has shaped how we live today.

Choose three events from Section 29.5 that you believe have most shaped how we live today. Label them on the timeline below. Include the date, a one-sentence summary, and an illustration for each event. Draw a line from the event to the correct place on the timeline.

Explain how one of the events on your timeline has shaped how we live today.

PROCESSING

Interview one of the oldest, most interesting people you know and create a time-line of events that have shaped that person's life.

- Share some of the events from this chapter with your interviewee. Ask him or her to describe any of these events that he or she lived through.

- Have your interviewee identify the three historic events that had the greatest effect on his or her life.

- Ask the person to describe how these events have shaped his or her life.

- After the interview, place those three events on the timeline below. Include the date, a one-sentence summary, and an illustration for each event. Draw a line from each event to the correct place on the timeline.

- *On a separate sheet of paper,* write a short, three-paragraph essay explaining how each of the three events shaped your interviewee's life.

Preparing to Write: Analyzing Arguments

Rachel Carson and Norman Borlaug represent two very different positions in the debate over protecting our planet and feeding its population. Around the world, people continue to wrestle with the same questions. Fill in the chart to organize the ideas behind the arguments.

	Position on Protecting the Environment	Position on Feeding the Population
Rachel Carson		
Norman Borlaug		
Agribusiness companies		
Organic farmers		

Writing Debate Arguments

Take a position in the debate about this question: *Can people balance feeding the population with protecting the environment?* Write three arguments for your position. If your position is "yes," argue how people can achieve this balance. If your position is "no," argue why people cannot achieve this balance.

Use this rubric to evaluate your arguments. Make changes in your arguments if you need to.

Score	Description
3	The three arguments address the debate question directly. The arguments are convincing. There are no spelling or grammar errors.
2	The arguments address the debate question. There are few spelling or grammar errors.
1	The arguments do not address the debate question. They are not convincing. There are many spelling or grammar errors.

Timeline Skills

Analyze the Unit 9 timeline in your book. Also think about what you have learned in this unit. Then answer the following questions.

1. Which territories did the United States acquire during this period of time? How many years did it take to acquire all of these lands?

2. What was the Grange? During which decade did it have the greatest impact?

3. During this time period, what important victories occurred in the conservation movement and in the fight to end child labor?

4. How long did the Spanish-American War last? What conflict arose out of the war, and how long did it last?

5. How did Andrew Carnegie's life change in 1901? How did this change affect the American people?

6. Why did the United States want to control a 10-mile-wide zone in Panama in 1903?

7. When was the NAACP formed, and what is its purpose?

8. What are two important facts about John D. Rockefeller during this time period?

9. How did the United States involve itself in world affairs in 1917 and then isolate itself in 1920?

Critical Thinking

Use the timeline and the chapters in the unit to answer the following questions.

10. Who do you think had the greatest impact on the United States during the Progressive era? Explain your choice.

11. Which of the U.S. territorial acquisitions during this time period was the most controversial? Explain your opinion.

12. Do you agree with the U.S. Senate's refusal to approve the Treaty of Versailles? Why or why not?

13. If you could add three more events to this timeline, which would they be? List each event, and explain why you think it is important enough to add to the timeline.

    a.

    b.

    c.

Chapter 1
7: Chief Luther Standing Bear, in Valerius Geist, *Buffalo Nation: History and Legend of the North American Bison* (Stillwater, MN: Voyageur Press, 1998).

Chapter 3
27: William Bradford, "The Mayflower Compact," adopted Nov. 11, 1620, at www.constitution. org. Ibid.

Chapter 4
35: Jonathan Edwards, in Giles Gunn, *Early American Writing* (New York: Penguin Books, 1994). Jonathan Mayhew, in John Wingate Thornton, *The Pulpit of the American Revolution: Or, the Political Sermons of the Period of 1776* (Boston: Gould and Lincoln, 1860), at www.books.google.com.

Chapter 5
49: Henry Wadsworth Longfellow, "Paul Revere's Ride," at www. bartleby.com.

Chapter 7
65: Joseph Plumb Martin, *Memoir of a Revolutionary Soldier: The Narrative of Joseph Plumb Martin* (Mineola, NY: Dover Pub., 2006).

Chapter 9
81: James Madison, *The Federalist*, at www.bartleby.com. **87:** Abigail Adams, in a letter to John Adams, May 7, 1776, at www.thelizlibrary. org.

Chapter 10
95: Thomas Jefferson, in "The Virginia Statute for Religious Freedom," Jan. 16, 1786, at www.lva.virginia.gov. **96:** Ibid.

Chapter 11
104: George Washington, in "Washington's Farewell Address," 1796, at www.bartleby.com.

Chapter 13
124: Davy Crockett, *A Narrative of the Life of David Crockett of the State of Tennessee* (Baltimore: E.L. Carey and A. Hart, 1834), at www.books.google.com.

Chapter 15
144: James Polk, in *Encyclopædia Britannica,* at www.britannica. com.

Chapter 18
171: Henry David Thoreau, *Walden or Life in the Woods* (New York: E. P. Dutton and Co., 1912).

Chapter 21
201: Abraham Lincoln, 1858, at www.bartleby.com. **202:** John Quincy Adams, *Memoirs of John Quincy Adams, Comprising Portions of His Diary from 1795 to 1848,* Vol. 5, ed. Charles Francis Adams (Philadelphia: J. B. Lippincott and Co., 1875), at www.books.google.com.

Chapter 22
217: Elijah Babbit, in Stephen Berry, *House of Abraham: Lincoln and the Todds, A Family Divided by War* (New York: Houghton Mifflin Co., 2007).

Chapter 23
225: Lyndon Johnson, in Juan Williams, *Eyes on the Prize: America's Civil Rights Years, 1954–1965* (New York: Viking, 1987).

Chapter 24
236: Sitting Bull, in Robert M. Utley, *Sitting Bull: The Life and Times of an American Patriot* (New York: Holt Paperbacks, 1993).

Chapter 25
241: *Chicago Tribune,* in Wayne Moquin and Charles Van Doren, eds., *The American Way of Crime: A Documentary History* (New York: Praeger, 1976). **245:** Thomas Edison, in Randall Stross, *The Wizard of Menlo Park: How Thomas Alva Edison Invented the Modern World* (New York: Crown Pub., 2007).

Chapter 27
267: "Declaration of Dependence by the Children of America in Mines and Factories and Workshops," in Hugh D. Hindman, *Child Labor: An American History* (New York: M. E. Sharpe, Inc., 2002).

Photographs

Cover: Greg Pease/Getty Images
Title page: Greg Pease/Getty Images

Chapter 1
5: Stephen J. Krasemann/Photo Researchers, Inc.

Chapter 13
122: Library of Congress

Art

Chapter 1
9: Doug Roy

Chapter 3
22: Doug Roy

Chapter 6
53: Len Ebert

Chapter 7
58–63: Len Ebert

Chapter 8
76–77: Doug Roy

Chapter 9
84: QYA Design Studio

Chapter 11
105–106: Gary Undercuffler

Chapter 12
111–116t: Gary Undercuffler

Chapter 14
128–131: Gary Undercuffler

Chapter 16
153: Doug Roy

Chapter 18
172–175: Gary Undercuffler

Chapter 21
201br: Gary Undercuffler
205: Gary Undercuffler

Chapter 22
213: Gary Undercuffler

Chapter 24
233: Doug Roy

Chapter 26
247: Doug Roy
248–251: Doug Roy

Chapter 27
263–265: Rosiland Solomon

Chapter 28
271: Doug Roy